dear lily

Engage Your Core &

Other Lessons for a

Healthy, Happy &

Well-lived Life

Your dreams create
your reality
all my love
♡ dr. lindsey

Lindsey Mansueto

Dedication

This book is dedicated to my amazing, supportive family. I am blessed. Thank you for your encouragement and guidance.

To my partner: What a wonderful life we are creating with intention. I am so grateful to you, and I will love you forever.

To my kids, Mia and Max: Continue to allow your dreams to create your reality and always know how much Daddy and I love you.

Acknowledgment

I would like to acknowledge my family, friends, staff members, and practice members; you continually inspire me. May each of you continue the pursuit of wellness, with love leading the way.

I am forever grateful to my amazing employees (past and present) who help me live my passion and serve our community by providing a safe place for holistic healing.

If you are reading these words, I wish you robust health, abundant wealth, and eternal love. Please know that I am proud of you for taking this step for your self-improvement… especially if it is your first.

Contents

About the Author

Dr. Lindsey Mansueto is a chiropractic physician who graduated from *Palmer College of Chiropractic* in 2007 with a Magna Cum Laude degree in Pre-Professional Biology from *Florida Institute of Technology*. Since opening *Flemington Chiropractic Center's* doors in May of 2013, Dr. Lindsey has built what is now known as one of the most leading *Chiropractic & Wellness centers* in Hunterdon County. She has won several awards, including *"Most Promising New Business"* and voted '*Hunterdon Happenings*' *"BEST Chiropractor"* for six out of the last seven years (2015, 2016, 2018, 2019, 2020 & 2021 – and voted in the Top 3 in 2017).

In 2018, she expanded her practice to the newly renovated suite 103 and added more staff to accommodate her patients' demands. Practices like *Cupping, Reiki, Healing Touch, Orthotics,* and *Aromatherapy* were added.

Dr. Lindsey feels that the human approach is important to help one heal and live at optimal levels of their health and well-being. She continues to give back to her community in big and small ways by participating yearly in the *Flemington Food Pantry Food Drive*, raising money for *Hunterdon Hospice* as well as spearheading community outreach initiatives.

In 2019, she set forth a proclamation with *Betsy Driver* to declare *September Drug-Free Pain Awareness Month* in *Hunterdon County*. Dr. Lindsey held an open discussion at the *Stangl Factory Farmers Market* for the community to receive education about non-invasive holistic therapies that provide relief without painful surgery or addictive opioids.

She also spoke as part of a panel for the *Force of Change Women's Conference* in November 2019, accompanied by the *American Red Cross* in discussing stress reduction and pain management for women entrepreneurs.

Dr. Lindsey's passion is empowering her patients to fearlessly focus on the life they wish to create. She teaches systematic journaling, a focus on intention, and how to not internalize the stress of modern-day living. This love of self-care helped launch *The Lifestyle Center*- a healing space where people can come together for group workshops, meditations, and energy work.

Anything Dr. Lindsey does, she does with one goal in my mind: not only the alleviation of pain but to inspire her patients to become active participants in their own well-being. She is honored and humbled to provide an opportunity, tools, and support for her patients seeking holistic care.

She loves educating, staying active, as well as spending time with her adoring family!

Chapter 1

Uncovering the Sinister
Truth of Life

"As long as greed is stronger than compassion, there will always be suffering."

– Rusty Eric

To live an amazing life is the dream. To explore the smorgasbord of experience. To feel deep joy. To flourish and soar. Given the opportunity, there's little you wouldn't do or give to make that dream come true.

Yet, when it comes to taking charge of your own life, it is often more complex in practice than in theory. Social conditioning, right from when you're just a small baby, can block your way. This conditioning can have lifelong consequences as it informs and trains our brains, desires, and outcomes.

Before you understand its effects, it's important to

learn what social conditioning is. It is the process through which individuals develop a set of beliefs, desires, and behaviors, those that meet the approval of either society as a whole or by groups within it.

Surprisingly, social conditioning is ubiquitous. Everyone is influenced, often subconsciously, by the people, structures, and systems that surround them. From parents to teachers, the community to media, politicians to religion, and even the books we read. This conditioning is constantly at work. Simply open your eyes, and it becomes difficult to overlook. You will notice it in action, in the nooks and crannies of every interaction and assumption.

For example, as a child, your mom may have emphasized that breakfast is the most important meal of the day. In this case, she likely instilled in you that skipping this meal will harm your health.

Have you ever questioned reality?

How many of us have ever thought about the reason and veracity for this belief?

Not many, that's for sure!

Do you know why?

It's because you, along with those from past generations, blindly follow a set of beliefs without any reasoning.
In reality, this phrase was born as a marketing tactic. It was
a catch cry used to sell more breakfast cereal, not because
there was peer-reviewed literature to support the claim.

So much of what we do, believe, and how we behave
is narrated to us, making us *the readers* of our books of life
instead of *the author*.

By the end of this book, you will feel empowered to
make a crucial decision; is social conditioning serving you,
so you should stay your course, or is it time to run a different
race?

Stereotypical Social Norms and You

Let's look at some stereotypical social norms to help
you identify how this is already playing out in your life. Ones
that you, along with others, have been conditioned to automatically practice:

No. 1 – Blending In

The first is blending in. Answer this question:

How many times have you been told not to stand out,

not to be different?

I'm sure you've heard this sentence, or something with the same sentiment, uttered at least once in your lifetime. Be it at home, at school, in your workplace, or within your group of peers.

The norm states that to get along, you should blend in with everyone. This invariably leads to self-consciousness and suppresses your uniqueness, your gifts, and your true radiant beauty.

No. 2 - Caring About What Others Think

Secondly, excessively caring for what others think and say about you is likely a predominant fear. It is for many people.

Being fearful about the judgment of others can be a thought that lingers, constantly niggling in the back of your mind. This inevitably transforms you into a people pleaser; you become trapped in concerns about what people might think or say about you.

Getting comfortable with not being liked by everybody is a great lesson, especially if learned at a young age. It will set you free!

No. 3 – Playing It Safe

Thirdly, the norm that you must always play it safe in life is prevalent. It may be why you curbed your creative, wild and beautiful ideas to stick with safer and supposedly credible alternatives. Yet, that safety will inevitably sap your heart and energy. It is but another limiting belief.

Many people have made it big with their crazy wild ideas. They live a life they love because they chose not to play it safe. They took calculated risks, resulting in incredible personal payoffs and fulfillment.

For example, Amelia Earhart became the first female aviator pilot to fly a solo trip in 1928. She made history by being the sixteenth woman in the world to get a pilot's license.

Earhart was a true underdog trying to find her place in a male-dominated industry. Yet, she set world records after beginning her career in 1922. In 1931, Earhart earned global recognition by flying at an altitude of 18,415 ft. Not only did she build a reputation as a competent pilot, but she also left a lasting legacy that paved the way for other female pilots.

Amelia Earhart was hailed as an aviation pioneer. Her daring adventures earned her the moniker of *Lady Lindy* after famed aviator, Lindenburg, who was known as *Lucky Lindy*. Earhart not only set records; she aspired to complete previously unachieved feats.

She was the first woman to fly across the Atlantic Ocean in 1928. After her first transatlantic flight, Earhart became more ambitious. She began planning to circumnavigate the Earth by traversing the Equator. At the time, such a trip had never been attempted by any pilot.

Sadly, Earhart and her plane, along with her team of brilliant navigators, Captain Harry Manning, Fred Noonan, and Paul Mantz, disappeared in 1937. Today, their disappearance is still clouded in mystery. Only speculations remain.

Earhart knew this journey would be accompanied by significant risk. When asked about the dangers of the flight prior to takeoff, she was quoted as saying, *"Please know that I am aware of the hazards. I want to do it because I want to do it."*

So you see, taking the bumpy road might look dangerous. It may be fraught with perils. But as long as you are passionate about your quest, you can set down your worries.

Ask yourself, *how many people do you know who died doing exactly what they loved most?*

Once you manage to find your calling and passion, you'll feel compelled and uplifted, inspired, and driven, regardless of potential obstacles. You'll likely reach your destination, even if it takes some time. Even if you don't, you'll experience an incredible, regret-free journey because you dared to travel the path you were destined for. The joy of doing what you love will be palpable.

If you think about it with clarity and truth, the things that hold you back are steeped in self-limiting beliefs. Your fears can deter you from living the life you desire and deserve.

Corruption and Greed in Society

Money and greed are powerful elements, with enormously corrupting influences on people across the world. Money is seen as equal to having power. This stokes the insatiable lust for wealth and financial authority. As a result, people, businesses, media, and institutions have focused solely on the drive to create and hoard profits, wherever and however they can, regardless of the consequences.

We are deeply entangled in the process of capitalism — buying and selling within the market — that we cannot imagine life being any other way. Consumption and consumerism dominate the social discourse, aspiration, and broad political agenda. This practice hogs and colors the limelight.

The *stability of life* is nothing but a mere illusion. No matter how rich one is, one can aim to become considerably richer. By our evolutionary nature, we constantly crave more. It's what led to the creation and refinement of the wheel.

On a general basis, this is one motivation behind our drive; the desire to want more and be more. It's what pushes us to pursue the *next* best job, the *next* best car, a *bigger* house, and so the cycle repeats.

Greedily grabbing bigger and brighter opportunities has become a wafer-thin replacement for the true meaning of life. Yet, for most, the more that ambition exceeds station, the more corrupt one is likely to become.

It's no secret that we, humans, inherently admire money and power. It's what most desire to hold firmly in the palm of their hands. But pause for a moment to reflect; money is destroying the world.

The obsession with money, gambling, shopping, purchasing lottery tickets — the constant accrual of material objects — is not only real and prominent, but it has also led to the creation of many addictions. Breaking free from these addictions is challenging.

Smoking Addiction – What You Should Know

Did you know that smoking is one of the most prevalent addictions of all time? Nicotine dependence means you are biologically dependent on this substance, even though you may know it is causing you harm.

Nicotine alters the brain, producing physical and mood-altering effects that deliver temporary pleasure. This leads to cravings for further cigarettes or chewing tobacco. Indulging then creates further dependence. At the same time, quitting tobacco use can be difficult. Stopping can trigger significant withdrawal symptoms, including irritability and anxiety, sweating and nausea, mood swings and headaches, coughing and insomnia, weight gain, and intense cravings for nicotine.

But it's not just the nicotine in tobacco that causes harm. While nicotine dependence is one concern, the toxic effects of tobacco should not be overlooked. Studies show that smokers have substantially higher rates of heart disease, stroke, lung cancer, and death when compared to nonsmokers. If you smoke, I hope this gives you a reason to pause.

Regardless of how long you've smoked, choosing a smoke-free life will rejuvenate your health, along with your life expectancy.

If you are serious about quitting smoking, I recommend reading or listening to *The Illustrated Easy Way for Women to Stop Smoking: A Liberating Guide to a Smoke-Free Future* by *Allen Carr*. Also known as *The Allen Carr Easyway Method,* this book smooths the process of quitting. Carr explains how we are conditioned to believe that quitting smoking will be too difficult. This social conditioning is purposeful and manipulative, so you give up before you try.

The striking fact is this; the same corporations that make cigarettes also make smoking cessation aids.

Really?

These companies profit from you, whether you are content in your habit or are trying to quit. As with other decisions in your life, the first step to quitting is to control your impulses while you make important decisions.

Ask yourself, *"Will this decision bring me closer to my goal?"*

Ensure you hold a serious intention. Being aware of this will prevent you from being sidetracked and propel you toward your desired goal.

Despite all the negative publicity, the cigarette market is still worth $816 billion. The industry sells nearly 5.5 trillion cigarettes to one billion smokers globally. The number of people who smoke is projected to rise to 1.64 billion by 2025.[1]

What's terrifying is that tobacco companies are profiting from your suffering. You likely don't realize that your eventual death is also being monetized with every cigarette you purchase. One report showed that tobacco companies make a profit of roughly USD 9,000 from every smoker's demise.[2]

Have you ever wondered why tobacco companies label their cigarette packs with "smoking kills?"

This enables them to steer clear from lawsuits and avoid responsibility for the dire consequences of smoking.

Lack of awareness here is not the issue. Rather it's consumers who choose, for whatever reason, to ignore or deny the gravity of the situation.

The harsh reality is that people with addictions will often not realize how their actions unintentionally feed their

---

[1] https://www.thelancet.com/journals/lancet/article/PIIS0140-6736(15)60264-1/fulltext#:~:text=If%20recent%20trends%20remain%20unchanged,%C2%B76%20billion)%20in%202025.
[2] https://www.ncbi.nlm.nih.gov/books/NBK99238/

habits. If prices rise, smoking often takes priority, while cut-backs are made in other areas. Cigarette and big tobacco companies use this to hold their monopoly.

To keep profits high, tobacco companies willingly spend money on marketing, especially in vulnerable and underdeveloped countries.[3]

For example, populations within third-world countries are generally less aware of cigarettes' detrimental effects on their health. Media depictions there also spin cigarettes in a positive light.

It seems like there is really no end in sight for the profitability of the tobacco companies as they look for growth in new markets around the world.

On the other hand, some are advised to quit. These people sometimes even wish to but face trouble controlling their impulses.

---

[3] https://www.statista.com/topics/1593/tobacco/

Addictions & the Lengths that People Go to Accommodate Them

Addiction is a psychological and physical inability to stop yourself from indulging in an activity, drug, or substance, even though it's detrimental to wellbeing. The term does not only refer to hard substance dependence like heroin, cocaine, or alcohol.

Some addictions involve the inability to stop overindulging in activities such as eating, shopping, gambling, and even working. Whether a shopaholic, an alcoholic, or a chain-smoker, people are driven to "get their fix" and continue the supply that sustains them. But, sometimes, people resort to stealing, physical violence, manipulation, and other undesirable acts in order to satisfy strong addictions.

Demi Lovato, the famed singer and former Disney child star, has been candid with her substance use disorder. She has opened up about her past, revealing that as her music career grew, so, too, did her substance abuse.

Her battle with addiction is ongoing, and she has been in and out of rehab. Her active addiction began in 2010. As for many others, it began with the abuse of prescription medication. In her case, Adderall. Overuse of alcohol and hard drugs like cocaine and heroin also grew. Lovato's drug abuse has been coupled with an eating disorder, as well as mental health issues.

Before being diagnosed with bipolar disorder (BPD), Lovato was prone to binge eating, extensive drug use, and extreme alcohol abuse. However, even after seeking professional help by checking into rehab, Lovato continued to crave drugs. Even when she knew others did not approve of it, she still indulged in her vices. Like many addicts, she went to extreme lengths to hide her addiction from the public and people around her.

In her tell-all documentary, *Stay Strong,* Lovato honestly explains how, even while publicly espousing the virtues of attending rehab, she was indulging in substances like cocaine and heroin on a daily basis.

She also resorted to violence, once choosing to punch a singer who had worked with her for telling others about her substance use.

"I didn't feel anything. I didn't feel guilty, and I didn't feel embarrassed. I would sneak out, get drugs. I

would fake my drug tests with other people's pee, and I'd lie straight to their faces. It's embarrassing to look back at the person that I was," Lovato explained.

In 2018, Lovato tried to overdose on drugs. While timely medical intervention saved her life, Lovato's behavior didn't change. She kept walking along the same path until her entire team delivered an ultimatum.

"It was not a matter of if they were going to leave; it was 'We are leaving. There is no more we can do for you,'" she said about the confrontation. Luckily, Lovato wanted to keep her team more than her drugs.

Lovato has celebrated one year of sobriety. Her recovery has been slow and peppered with relapses. But she's been able to overcome most of her demons. Even with a high-pressure job and the constancy of the public eye, she has embraced sobriety and continues to inspire and support others who travel a similar path.

The lessons you can learn from Demi Lovato's experience are many. However, two things stand out for me: Not everything that shines is gold, and it's solely up to you to rise from the ashes.

Scientists are only now beginning to see the link between dopamine production and the use of substances like drugs and money. They are powerful addictions as they possess the ability to trigger good feelings within you. They drive your desire to relieve the experiences they trigger because they feel so good.

The frightening part is that while certain addictions like cocaine or heroin can kill, money won't. Money won't tarnish your physical health. Realizing that you're addicted and engaged in its abuse then becomes extremely difficult.

In fact, for the longest time, money addiction was overlooked. Money addicts tend to blend in. They may even be revered just as wealth is within our society. These addicts, like others, have few boundaries and poor morals. Content to brainwash en masse, derail democratic politics, and hijack human spirituality should it support their desire to accumulate more. Unfortunately, we have been conditioned to cooperate with the greedy and corrupt. I believe the consequences have been dire, empowering these addicts to sabotage and ruin our society and others.

We have become so accustomed to remaining quiet, suppressing our voices, and not standing up against power-hungry maniacs and addicts. In this silence, we have handed over our leverage and power. It's time that people like you and I unite and demand large-scale change.

Money doesn't make one happy; it never has, and it never will. But this proposition is peddled daily, marketed regularly and fiercely. Owning a huge nest egg will not decrease self-loathing. Holding material possessions will not diminish loneliness. Accruing excess won't fill the physical, mental, emotional, and spiritual abyss.

We need to understand the importance of contentedness and enjoyment. We need to thrive throughout life's journey instead of waiting until we are *"rich enough"* to take delight in ourselves and our experiences. We also need to teach this to the next generation.

So tell me, are you with me in this fight?

Chapter 2

Discipline Is The New Fun

"Discipline is choosing between what you want now and what you want most."

– Abraham Lincoln

Emotions can undoubtedly play an important role in how you think and behave. They can be both short-lived and long-lasting. For example, a flash of annoyance at a coworker can be short-term, whereas enduring grief over losing a loved one is often long-term.

The emotions you feel can compel you to take action and influence life's decisions, both big and small.

Emotions serve a wide variety of purposes. They can be fleeting, powerful, complex, persistent, draining, or even life-changing. An array of emotions help us figure out what we do or don't want. This is why colossal significance ought to be placed on being emotionally aware.

Understanding Anxiety

Different situations release different emotions in each of us. For instance, when you're faced with a nerve-wracking situation, you might feel a rush of anxiety. This is why you need to identify your triggers – the activities that make you anxious.

Keep in mind that experiencing anxiety occasionally is a normal part of life. However, people with anxiety disorders recurrently suffer from intense, excessive, and persistent worry and terror with regard to everyday situations.

As a matter of fact, when ongoing, anxiety is classified as a mental health condition. It is incredibly common and known to trigger feelings of uneasiness, fear, or tension.

Common Symptoms of Anxiety

Some common and some overlooked symptoms of anxiety include:

- Excessive sweating

- Trembling

- Fatigue

- Trouble sleeping (insomnia)

- Feeling nervous or restless

- Hyperventilation

- An urge to run away

- Avoidance of situations that trigger anxiety

- Increased heart rate

- Gastrointestinal issues

- Trouble concentrating

- Problems contemplating anything other than present worries

For some people, anxiety can also cause extreme physical symptoms such as panic attacks and chest pain.

Triggers of Anxiety

Anxiety has many potential prompts. Each individual has a unique set of triggers, and one precipitator might cause a flare one day, yet not another. However, there are common provocateurs. I am sharing these to enhance your awareness:

- Health issues

- Negative thinking

- Medication

- Financial concerns

- Caffeine

- Skipping meals

- Social events

- Stress

Experiencing an anxiety disorder does more than make you worry. It can prompt or worsen physical or other psychological conditions. Understandably, anxiety can lead to depression. The combination can spiral into deeper ill health, substance misuse, and, at times, suicide.

Identifying your triggers, then, is a crucial step toward managing them. If you can place a pause or strategy before you become swamped by the downward cascade, it's possible to avoid or alleviate suffering.

Why Do You Need to Identify What Makes You Anxious?

Identifying a problem is always the first step to triumphing over it. Naturally, when you're not aware of a problem's root cause, you can't begin to repair or work toward a resolution. Thus, identifying what stirs anxiety within empowers you to gently refrain while enabling you to find healthy solutions for management.

For some people, activities like sitting for a difficult exam, speaking in public, or being intimate for the first time can cause anxiety. Apprehension and fear relate to potential performance.

Running away from a problem is never the best answer. Yet, many people who suffer from anxiety choose this option. As I just mentioned, refraining can calm anxiousness while you find a healthy solution. It does not replace the need to move forward toward healing. By simply providing a temporary pause, you can dive deeper, learn to tranquilize panic, and uncover the power that lives and thrives within you and all of us.

With this in mind, my question is, *why not stand up*

to your fears?

Once you have successfully identified your triggers, you can begin the creation of a considered plan. To complete this roadmap requires management. So, gather your courage. Understand that healing is a process, not an event; recovery takes time and effort.

The next section will emancipate you from the shackles. The aim: To empower you to stand up to your fears. In doing so, trepidation will falter, and anxiety will abate.

How to Manage Your Anxiety?

There are efficient and trusted ways to manage, even overcome, your anxiety. Here are my favorites; those I've seen work for my patients time and again.

Acceptance

Accept what troubles you, as acceptance is the first step to recovery. Acknowledging that you suffer from anxiety will open your mind to seeking help while minimizing shame. Seek professional help as early as possible because anxiety, like many disorders, can become harder to treat over time.

Work with a reliable therapist or a mental health specialist who has the required training. Different techniques may be incorporated, such as talk therapy, cognitive behavioral therapy, or journaling. Often discussing problems with a trusted, objective expert eases the mind and allows you to locate and vent suppressed emotions.

Be open to self-help. Write down when anxiety becomes most noticeable.

Were there triggers?

What symptoms did you face?

What provided relief?

Record this information. Consider feedback from those closest to you. Journal your feelings; this will allow you to revisit your experience without judgment. You can learn a great deal about yourself by re-reading previous notes or journal entries.

Nurture Your Body

Nurture your physical self. I cannot stress this enough; *a healthy body sustains a healthy mind.*

Eat regular, well-balanced meals. Exercise often.

Consistently focus on self-care. Avoid alcohol and drugs. Prioritize restorative sleep.

Perform mindful breathing. This step interrupts the anxiety spiral and helps you to remain calm. Establishing a practice of deep, conscious breathing is grounding - a few minutes each day, and in times of bubbling anxiousness, is sufficient. You'll soon appreciate the vast wonders delivered by a simple inhaling, exhaling exercise.

I recommend learning and following *The Wim Hof Breathing Method.* This technique stimulates the vagus nerve to switch your physiology from one of sympathetic dominance (the "flight/fight/freeze reaction") to one of parasympathetic power (the "rest and recovery" response). This enables you to respond to stressors around you calmly. There are plenty of guided videos on this method on YouTube. Include this practice in your routine when you wake up to begin your day correctly.

We cannot medicate our way out of our problems. You cannot take insulin for type II diabetes and continue to gorge on sugary foods. You must be aware that taking opioids may temporarily mitigate pain, but it does not solve the underlying problem. In our pill-happy environment, it's oft-touted that one pill will massively alter your life. The marketing dollars spent to convince you of this are immense.

In my humble opinion, the people who make the most progress are those who amend their lifestyle and include ways to ample self-care. I see this in my patients time and again. Meal prep, stretching, healthy water intake, mental health counseling, journaling, rest, and breathwork are just a few ways to practice self-care successfully. This truly can calm anxiety and hand back control of your health and your life.

Retrain Your Mind

By avoiding scenarios, you introduce and magnify fear in everyday life. Over time, this will manifest greater anxiety to the point where it starts to feed upon you hungrily.

Instead, coach yourself to approach difficult and stressful situations. Assess places and scenarios you have previously avoided. While doing so, indulge in meaningful self-talk. Ask questions like:

Is my worry real?

Am I inventing or exacerbating these scenarios?

Could this be happening due to an unknown fear or

past experience?

How likely is this to happen in real life?

Counter negative thoughts with positive reaffirming statements such as *"I may feel anxious, but I am still able to do this."*

Think of occasions where you have coped well. Let that thought be the uplifting force that carries you forward.

Don't Give In Immediately

Practice tolerating small doses of anxiety without seeking an immediate escape. This may take some time, which is perfectly fine. Then, with determination, you'll build stronger resilience. You will become more conformable in being uncomfortable, and, as you do, the discomfort will paradoxically decline.

It is also helpful to thank your mind for the anxiety that you feel. A well of rising anxiousness is meant as a protective mechanism; it has simply gone awry. Start with this statement:

"Thank you for triggering my fight/flight response to raise your concern about my public speaking engagement. I will harness this power to meet its demands and deadlines. I

can now practice being my most confident self while I give that presentation."

Practice Mindfulness and Grounding

One of my favorite ways to de-stress and deal with anxiety is to immerse myself in nature. To place my feet on the ground and perform the ritual of grounding.

It is a freeing, easy practice to incorporate. Slip off your shoes and steep your feet in the grass. Walk barefoot as you recite an affirmation or set a powerful intention.

My favorite intentions and affirmations include:

- *I am grounded.*

- *My spirit is grounded deep within the Earth.*

- *I am calm, strong, centered, and peaceful.*

- *I am able to let go of fear and trust that I am eternally safe.*

Have a Plan in Place

Last but not least, create a plan and execute it. In order to feel confident, competent, and relaxed, plan to and incorporate strategies regularly. This helps to embed and establish new, healthy habits.

Set realistic, meaningful goals for your life and identify the skills needed for their realization. Find out how you can acquire these skills, then build on them. Don't be afraid to learn through trial and error. Get help, even if it seems daunting. Start with one small step toward your goal. Rehearse until you feel ready to take the next small step or to embrace a whole new level.

Contain and calm your worry by using the steps in this book. That's why I wrote it! Surrender your concerns that you have little to no control over.

Use Social Media Mindfully

If you follow someone on social media and their posts trigger stress, anxiety, or invoke feelings of *"less than,"* unfollow, unfriend, or block them. Limit your exposure to anyone who makes you feel that you are not enough...

Even if that means unfollowing me. (Just joking! Follow me on social media. I'd love to connect!

@flemingtonchirocenter on IG, and

FlemingtonchiropracticCenter on FB.

Also, check out my personal page under *Lindsey Mansueto* on Tik Tok).

Back to this important point, though. Focus on what inspires happiness within you. Curate a social media feed that invites feelings of goodness, sufficiency and reaffirms your self-worth. Be careful and conscious as you create your social media feed. Your feed shows that which you follow and interact with, and so can be considered as a storyboard for what you allow.

Be Strong Enough to Cull

There's a popular quote I love which says, *"Before you diagnose yourself with depression or low self-esteem, make sure that you are not, in fact, just surrounded by assholes."*

Take this quote to heart. Distance yourself from people, places, and things that make you feel unworthy, unhappy, or unappreciated.

Gifting yourself this break will often create a virtual inhale, like drawing in a deep breath of revitalizing fresh air. We often become preoccupied with pleasing others or meeting expectations that are not ours. This can spark heaviness as we feel unworthy, unlovable, unimportant. The artificial notion that we're not living up to the expectations can be felt keenly, like the poison it is. Little wonder it can drive us to despair.

But, when you cull negative people from your life and instead surround yourself with positive peeps — those who see and love your uniqueness and truth your self-esteem and confidence will naturally and effortlessly begin to shift. As an added advantage, your anxiety will greatly ease.

Adopt a Problem Solving Approach

A powerful way to quell worry is by implementing a problem-solving approach—brainstorm possible solutions. Use pros and cons to decide on the best solution. Your journal makes a wonderful place to begin your brainstorming journey!

The fact is, if you stress out before something happens, you experience it twice. This has physical and psychological consequences, often without benefit. Save yourself from pre-anxiety by applying problem-solving techniques.

Positive Visualization

Positive visualization goes a long way toward helping manage your anxiety and stress. That's why Olympians have harnessed its power for decades. To begin this exploration with you, I'd love to share one of my favorite examples...

Imagine having an empty container where you can store all your worries. Now, picture yourself dumping your worries into the container. When you're done, mentally put on the lid. Screw it on tightly.

This simple visualization helps to remove negativity and clear your mind. With some practice, you will be able to do this effortlessly.

The steps in this chapter are designed to invite peace and happiness into your life, to replace old, inaccurate, and negative stories with ones that serve your wellbeing. Positivity is a potent repellent to anxiety because it counters the negativity that fear and stress generate. Remember: Adopting a positive mindset can transform your life! Look for the silver lining; it's everywhere.

Taking Control of Your Emotions

Life is all about choices; the choices you make are what truly define you. Often we rush to a rash decision based on emotion alone. But no feeling is everlasting, and, in your lifetime, you will experience various iterations. By taking control of your emotions and their inherent flux, you are better placed to make choices that serve and support you.

When it comes to your emotions, control is not the same as suppression. Attempting to ignore your sadness or pretend you don't feel pain won't make those feelings disappear. However, gaining emotional mastery will enhance your mental strength, which will instigate better choice-making.

I witness patients in my practice trying to stuff their emotions down deeply on a daily basis. I remind them that *"Issues get stuck in your tissues."* For example, people with upper back spasms are often dealing with stress. But they hurriedly move on, refusing to sit in the emotion, accept what they feel, and work on solutions to remedy the situation.

Those who experience psoas pain are typically dealing with communication problems in their personal lives. There is a good reason why this muscle is called the window to the soul. But if you refuse to look through the pane, it's nearly impossible to find an answer.

Remember, as we've discussed, the physical act of putting pen to paper to jot down how you feel can lighten the load. But I also have a bundle of techniques that will help you to move forward and heal. These powerful tools will support your wellbeing, just as they have helped my many patients.

Everyone can become better at regulating their emotions. Your part is to commit to regular practice with sincere dedication. My part is to show you how. That's what this chapter is about. Before we begin, ask yourself...

If you easily let your emotions overpower you, where will you stand?

You are the One in Charge

What's essential to understand is that *you* are the one who is entirely in charge of your mind; it is *you* who has power over your thoughts.

As humans, we are an outstanding species. We often overlook the skills innate to each of us. Sometimes, they have simply not surfaced or blossomed into their full potential. One of these core competencies is the ability to accomplish almost anything you put your mind to. This includes self-compassion.

Radical Self-Compassion

I would love for you to start practicing radical self-compassion, offering yourself comfort and understanding while focusing on all that you have accomplished instead of what you imagine you lack. We are all star beings; literally created from stardust! We are each evolving into a higher self that prioritizes self-love and self-compassion.

We can tap into the larger source to reclaim the unbreakable link we have with our ancestors, the universe, our deities, family members, and even our pets. We can ask for support to heal from past pain and trauma.

Remember that you are never alone in your trauma and hurt. All of us are suffering in our own ways. We need to be open with our emotions and sit in their uncomfortableness to find a way to move on truly.

I see a lot of internalized trauma rearing its ugly head and manifesting as dysfunction in the brain and body in my professional capacity.

Spiritual Re-parenting – The Easy Way

Spiritual re-parenting enables us to employ our emotions as a gateway to delve into trauma and recover. We allow ourselves to feel our feelings and then act as a loving parent guiding us to salvation.

The acronym RAIN provides guidance for this process. (I learned it from a meditation application called Calm, created by Tara Barch. It's available on iOS and android)

- **R**ecognize the feeling

- **A**ccept that you are feeling that way

- **I**nvestigate why you are feeling this way

- **N**urture yourself with love and compassion while you sit with your feelings

Give yourself permission to let go and heal. Move on.

You will not master this in one sitting or one day.

Years of trauma and pain can take seasons to nullify. So, be patient and compassionate while spiritually re-parenting yourself.

Build a Powerful Mind

We all have one of the most powerful tools known to humankind at our disposal, but many of us do not know how to wield that power. Yes, I'm talking about the human brain. Your mind is undoubtedly the most powerful and active organ in your body.

When you learn to control your mind, you will overcome incredible obstacles and achieve fantastic accomplishments. You are vastly more powerful than you believe!

So, how exactly do you build a strong and powerful mind?

If you are in a hurry, the answer might irritate you. It involves repetitively and regularly training your mind over time. Remember, patience and self-compassion are the keys here. You will not awaken with a feeble mindset and settle for evening slumber with an attitude of indestructible steel. But it will come. A stronger mindset is established by gradually challenging yourself to break free from your comfort zone, take risks, and test your boundaries.

If you have not yet achieved success, it is because it lies outside of your comfort zone. Embrace discomfort (yes, you can start small). It isn't easy, but by pushing yourself through struggles, you engage and magnify your power. If you don't, you will likely live with regret.

So, when you feel a negative, draining emotion such as anger or sadness, recall RAIN.

Acknowledge it, feel it, accept it even, but do not let emotion overpower you. Control your emotions by pausing for a moment and providing space to feel them. Once time is up, distract or immerse yourself with a mood-lightening activity and surrender the negativity to the universe.

Self-Discipline And How To Achieve It?

In the heart of a successful person lies self-discipline. Whether it's success in their professional or personal lives, it starts with an inherent ability to control one's self through discipline—the ability to keep thoughts, emotions, habits, and behaviors in check.

To achieve the lofty goals you set, it's important to

understand how to discipline yourself. This is the key ingredient in your recipe for success. It's interesting to note that
the virtues of self-discipline are not new. In fact, self-discipline has been a hot topic of discussion for thousands of
years, and it's been championed by some of the world's most
successful people.

Esther Pauline "Eppie" Lederer, commonly known
as Ann Landers, stated that, *"Self-discipline and self-
knowledge is the sure-footedness that comes with having
proved that you can meet life's challenges."*

Discipline is the conduit that connects dreams and
goals to achievement. Successful people leverage the art of
self-discipline by creating a foundational set of good habits
that raise the likelihood they will see things through.

Along with discipline, it's imperative to include ample hard work because both go hand in hand. I'm sure you've
heard the popular saying, *'hard work pays off.'* This couldn't
be more true. To achieve significant goals, you must be willing to invest whatever is demanded of you and reach beyond
mediocrity. Start working hard today to enjoy the fruits of
your labor tomorrow.

Let's dive into a discussion on the impactful ways to harness self-discipline in order to halt excuse-making, particularly in the face of temporary failure. This will supercharge your willpower and provide a happier and healthier life.

First and Foremost, Know Your Weaknesses

It's no surprise; we all have weaknesses. Whether they're snacks such as potato chips or chocolate chip brownies, or technology such as Facebook or Instagram, or the latest addictive game app, they all have similar effects on us. Acknowledge your shortcomings, whatever they are.

Too often, people either pretend their vulnerabilities are non-existent or cover up pitfalls in their lives. Own up to your flaws; you can't find a remedy until you accept them. Learn to be fearlessly authentic and imperfectly perfect.

Secondly, Be Stronger Than Life's Temptations

The famous saying, *"Out of sight, out of mind,"* should be a habit that you practice. It may seem trivial, but this phrase offers powerful advice.

By simply removing the biggest temptations from

your environment, you will critically improve your self-discipline. For example, if you wish to eat healthier, don't buy junk food. If you want to improve your productivity at work, turn off notifications and mute your cell phone. The fewer distractions you have, the more focused you will be.

Set yourself up for success by ditching unhelpful temptations. Replace these with activities or options that positively influence you, bringing you closer to success.

The Third Point on the List Is Goal Setting

Setting goals is vital, but why is that so? The answer is quite simple; if you list the goals you wish to accomplish, you can see where you currently stand and the steps needed to work toward them.

You must have a clear vision of what you want. It is normal for goals to morph as you accomplish them, but if you don't know how you wish to feel or what you want to accomplish, you will spin your wheels and quickly go nowhere. Even worse, if you don't know where you're headed, you'll easily lose your way. You may even get sidetracked or find yourself on an entirely different path.

Can you imagine a captain steering her ship without

a destination or map?

You also need to understand what success means to you to intuit your progress and work toward your specific goal. A clear plan outlines each step you must take in order to reach your goals. So, figure out who you are, what you care about, what you want, and plot an appropriate path. To do just that, mantras and positive reaffirmations can be great tools. Creating a mantra to keep yourself focused is a subtle way to keep your goal front of mind, motivate yourself, and inspire positivity.

My personal mantras include the following:

- *My dreams create my reality*

- *I choose robust health, abundant wealth, and eternal love*

- *I am grateful for all the abundant universe gives and all that I receive*

- *My life is now in total balance, and I am its master*

Fourth Is Being Organized

I know this one seems obvious. It's probably been

driven into your head by your parents, especially your mother. This is because being organized is a skill that every human being should equip themselves with.

Nurturing organizational skills has multiple benefits. It saves swathes of time, greatly reduces stress, increases productivity, creates a better work-life balance, and bequeaths energy and enthusiasm.

If you need help or motivation to get organized, check out shows like *Organizational Goddesses* or *Tidying Up with Marie Kondo* on Netflix. Marie Kondo's organizational system revolves around mindfulness and minimalism. She is a fount of knowledge! You really will learn a thing or two from her.

The Fifth Point Is Better Time Management

There are 24 hours in every day, but have you ever wondered how certain people manage to extract the most from every minute?

Believe it or not, no one has the power to slow down time. However, some exploit the power to *manage* their time effectively. It seems like they bend reality to their will, attracting an enviable effortlessness.

In order to manage your time better, start by evaluating the approximate time required to perform each task on your daily schedule. This translates into power as you set a time limit for each task.

This allows you to create a plan, then stick to it. Self-discipline is largely derived from our ability to manage our time effectively. Remember, Marie Kondo employs minimalism. Ensure the tasks on your list absolutely need to be there. If not, cull!

Last Is Gratitude

Many of us spend too much time wanting, desiring, lusting after. The habit of gratitude helps you move from incessantly craving what you don't have to appreciate what you do. Spend 10 minutes each day thanking the universe for everything that you're grateful for.

My personal routine is to think of three things I am grateful for before my feet touch the floor in the morning. Starting each day with a grateful heart is the way I choose to live my life.

Even if you feel there is nothing to be grateful for,

seek, and you shall find. Gratitude is a humbling feeling because it shifts focus from deprivation or incompleteness toward a state of abundance and wholeness.

To conclude, instead of toiling with the bare mini-
mum, dedicate your time to self-improvement and continu-
ous learning. When self-awareness and growth are not part
of the journey, unconscious self-sabotage can destroy
dreams and aspirations. Then, in frustration, people turn to
the outside world for blame.

I believe this to be an important contributor to the
world's current state and the many challenges we face. Unfortunately, a large percentage of the population acts from
their victimhood. Instead, it is possible to switch the play-
book and take the responsibility needed to foster real change.

Every day, patients tell me they don't have time to
stretch, drink water, exercise, etc. Those who don't make
time for wellness activities will eventually start making time
for doctor appointments. This is no one's choice but your
own, so choose wisely.

The path to the success that you desire isn't smooth,
nor is it easy; there will be bumps and hardships along the

way. Learn how to tackle these strategically, how to handle setbacks gracefully, and your life will change!

Activity – What Is Your Idea of Living?

Let me ask you this… *At the end of your life, what do you want your obituary to say?*

We need to focus on loving ourselves with generosity and kindness before we are truly able to do the same for others. To my mind, being disciplined with soul searching and in the development of a mindful presence, and owning my focus on active caring and inclusivity for all is what living is all about.

Please use the rest of this page to write down your idea of living.

_____

_____

_____

_____

_____

_____

_____

_____

_____

_____

_____

_____

_____

_____

Chapter 3

Don't Let the World Control You: You Control The World

"Don't adapt to the energy in the room. Influence the energy in the room."

I think no one explained this better than Matt Haig, the author of *Reasons to Stay Alive*. To paraphrase a popular paragraph from the book:

The world is increasingly designed to depress us.

Why?

Happiness isn't good for the economy. If we were happy with what we had, why would we need more?

Think about it. How do you sell an anti-aging moisturizer? You stoke fear and heighten concern around aging.

How do you encourage people to vote for a political party? You incite panic about immigration and other social matters.

How do you ensure people buy insurance? By instigating the angst that would be triggered by loss.

How do you promote plastic surgery? By highlighting a person's (perceived) physical flaws. And by redefining the meaning of beauty, so it becomes almost impossible to achieve naturally.

How do you raise viewership for a TV show? By convincing people, should they not, they will miss crucial information or regret the lost experience. Fear of missing out, also known as FOMO, is real.

How do you raise sales of a new smartphone? By making someone feel that, without this new tech, they will be left behind.

In the midst of this chaos and noise, to be calm becomes a revolutionary act. To be happy with your non-upgraded existence, rebellious. To be comfortable with your messy human self is simply not good for business.

The truth is clear and resonant.

This passage deserves to be unpacked to gain deeper insight. Then, armed with knowledge, we can spread awareness; that's the focus of this chapter.

But first, let me ask you two questions:

- *What's the first thing that enters your mind when you read this passage?*

- *Did it feel shocking to register the authenticity of it?*

The harsh truth is that many people don't realize how the capitalist world functions or the depths of deceit and manipulation used to engender massive profit.

Happiness, in this context, is a mere illusion. If it truly existed, overzealous consumerism would falter. People would not constantly seek that next new thing, be it a gadget, phone, car, house, or job. We deserve to feel that our jobs, businesses, and other sources of income provide security. But we don't.

The reason for this uneasiness is as simple as it is unscrupulous. The commercialized world constantly and convincingly sells you the idea that you always need more to be happy. The eight to nine-hour workday is extremely profitable for big companies, not because of the work that people achieve within the allotted time, but because it purchases happy public.

By transforming free time into a scarce commodity, people pay more for convenience, gratification, and other forms of relief just to wrest back time. TV commercials become compelling—ambition outside of work withers.

Sadly, we've been led into a culture that's been strategically engineered to leave us tired, hungry for indulgence, and willing to pay handsomely for convenience and entertainment. This scenario has bred a vague dissatisfaction with our lives, perpetuating a craving for things we don't possess. We buy because we wish to fill a void. But, after the initial, short-lived high subsides, retail therapy leaves us hankering for our next hit. The cycle becomes addictive.

This world, if you allow it, will consume you entirely. The distraction and allure of lust and money have punctured the most sacred parts of our individual and collective spirit and mind. Your everyday routine and desires may seem normal, but that's simply a reflection of the standard. The process slowly creates physical illness. And, maybe imperceptibly at first, it depletes mental stability.

For instance, you might not suddenly experience cough or heart palpitations, but your inner-self will drain by individual drops. Many of the marketing and persuasive tactics are subversive, subtle, and ubiquitous. This is why we each must look outside the box, seek depth of understanding, and pay close attention to the hidden messages.

It's the only way to take back control instead of continuing to surrender the remote.

So, how can you re-establish command of your life? More specifically, emotional understanding and control?

Let's take a look.

Emotional Control

Emotional control is a facet of emotion regulation; it primarily refers to the management of one's emotional responses. It is the ability to exert influence over emotions by the use of behavioral strategies.

Not knowing how to accomplish sovereignty results in being swept along the preordained path. That's why mastery of self and one's affairs is rare. Quite often, it takes a long time for people to realize that they alone do not control and direct their own lives. Some fail to see or accept it, preferring the comfort of their denial.

But denial gifts others power. It allows organizations to control their time, thoughts, and future. The accepted societal path is adhered to because that's what is expected. It's the conditioned norm. I believe the vast majority have given up control of their lives in deference to the standards set by the world.

Suppose you are an 18-year old with an amazing business plan and a willingness to establish a commercial enterprise that benefits the community. No bank will loan you $100K. However, if you are an 18-year old with zero work ethic and poor habits who decides to major in art history, banks will line up to offer a loan for college. See the paradox? Once bogged down with a hefty loan, you become a slave to the bank. This forces you into a 9-5 job to pay back that debt.

Building a career that you detest to fulfill the expectations of others is common. So, you are starting a job you dislike because it pays well, staying in a loveless relationship for fear of being single, or working for decades as a reliable, uncomplaining, *"Good"* employee while settling for less instead of striving for that which you truly deserve. Each example has embedded at its root conditioning to living a robotic, mundane life.

These scenarios are instances of stepping into well-worn norms. Where power has been relinquished in submission to established Western world rules.

Ask yourself honestly, *Have you fallen into this trap?*

Maybe because you fear the unknown?

Do you repeat the same mistakes yet deny a lack of control?

Remember, when you were a kid, there existed unlimited potential. No life-changing choices had been made, and there were no commitments. Then, somewhere along the way, you realized the world wasn't how you hoped it would be. Maybe you conformed to society's expectations, stopped being yourself, and gave up on chasing your dreams?

I understand that we are each governed by the world around us, as well as our circumstances. We all have commitments and needs to attend to. So, making a drastic change can seem difficult, especially when many things are outside our control.

However, there are still critical pieces within your control; you simply need to open your eyes and your heart.

You can:

- Make a well-structured plan to leave the job you hate

- Control your wealth by managing your finances

- Depart an unhealthy relationship by working on your emotional stability

- Use feeling stuck as ammunition to figure out an exit strategy

There is much that can be achieved with proper planning!

I feel that the younger generation has a wholly different outlook on what a successful life means when compared to the older generation. Older generations were taught to work hard, find a spouse, buy a house, and retire with maybe ten years left to enjoy their 401Ks.

However, the younger generations are learning from those mistakes. Many realize it is ok to slow down, be present, feel deeply, have fun, and celebrate often. It is not irresponsible to prioritize pleasure on a daily basis. No one, while laying on their death beds, says, *"Wow, I wished I worked more and spent less time hanging out with loved ones and enjoying myself."*

Stop being so comfortable living an unfulfilling life; stop letting others control your life and your precious time. Have the courage to live life fearlessly, the way you want! Learn to live fully in appreciation of your authentic, beautiful self by practicing radical self-compassion.

Fortunately, it's never too late for you to change the course of your life. It's important to realize that to be happy, you must pursue your dreams, forge your own path, and be the captain of your ship. At the end of the day, life is about living your best, being happy, and remaining in control of the choices you make.

So, how can you wrench back emotional control?

Taking Back Emotional Control

For starters, indulge in constructive thinking and ask confronting questions like, *"Am I really in control, or am I being controlled?"*

This will help you reflect on your life and on the choices you've made, hold a spotlight on your behaviors and responses, and more.

Then ask yourself, *"Do you really want to be swept along with the masses or strive hard to foster change?"*

When you open your eyes, your mind, and your heart, you will begin to see the endless possibilities that await you, the hurdles you can overcome, the chances you can take, and the changes you can bring to pass.

Staying *"woke"* at all times is as important as breathing. This is because if you're not aware of what's happening around you, you will remain stagnant, unable to move ahead and take ownership of your life.

Here is a list of my favorite actionable steps to empower you to take back emotional control.

Step One – Stop Being a Target for Digital Marketing

Have you noticed that your social media accounts become ablaze with potential solutions immediately after performing an internet search? This is by design; the continual fine-tuning of complex algorithms contrived to intuit your nature. The more information you feed the machine, the more complete the picture, the more persuasively you can be sold on an item or an idea.

How did — and does — this happen? The internet has infiltrated our lives. It has tactfully weaponized our narratives and created villains and heroes. In some cases, it has brought us closer but mostly has driven us further apart.

If you think about it, our want to connect and live online has created ample collateral damage, especially when it comes to privacy. Many of us have been willing collaborators in this privacy invasion. We share our lives on platforms like Facebook, Twitter, and Instagram. Each picture, share, like, and interaction tells the algorithm more about you; your desires, values, dreams. Apps with location services like Snapchat or your FitBit know where you are at all times.

This data is profitable! It enables advertisers to learn precisely how to appeal to you, to pull at your heartstrings, and loosen your purse strings. If you imagine I'm exaggerating, please watch the documentary *The Social Dilemma* on Netflix.

With this awareness, getting serious about your privacy becomes essential and urgent. Take control of your digital hygiene in the same way you should control your health, your savings, even your right to vote.

Purify your online experience by protecting yourself from advertisers. Ad blockers help to halt the display of adverts. Remember, the information collected about you is used to persuade and sell.

By avoiding ads designed to trigger your emotions, you can avoid being drawn into unnecessary conversations or purchases. Ad-block Plus is a great option. Change your Facebook settings by going into the Privacy options, so your brand preferences and interactions remain hidden.

Use two-factor authentication. This additional login step is available on popular social apps. It's a wonderful way to bolster security. Start using encrypted email and texting services. Lastly, download and install a VPN, as this allows you to browse the internet without your IP address tracked. Quality VPNs are not free, but I believe they are well worth the investment. You can share one across multiple devices.

Step Two – No Compromises on 'Me Time'

Your 'Me time' should be protected like a mother cares for her young one; without question or compromise.

This is explicit time dedicated to your fulfillment and enjoyment.

Sure, it can be tempting to compromise, especially when someone invites you to a fun social gathering! But we often compromise — whether our integrity, pride, values, or the time we devote to ourselves — that it becomes normalized. The practice of regular 'me time,' then, strengthens our self-worth muscle. That makes it easier when times get tough.

It's important to realize that you have the _full right to be selfish_ at times. If you only serve or conform to the wishes of others, you wind up feeling empty and become swept up in the societal storm we mentioned earlier: losing track of your dreams, goals, and self.

Start putting yourself first because you are your biggest investment. Allocate time to enjoy your own company and indulge. This can be a simple 10-minute meditation, a quick workout, or a relaxing hour spent lost in your latest read.

Quench your thirst for variety. Happiness and satisfaction need not only come from a shortlist. Why not pamper yourself with a luxurious visit to the salon? Binge-watch your favorite movies or TV series with friends. Head to the gym, regularly enjoy a great skincare routine, get some rest.

'Me time' is refreshing. This precious period will help you boost and recharge from the hustle and bustle of daily life. Remember, self-care is not selfish; it is necessary for a harmonious life.

Step Three – Remove Fear

The third step is to remove the fear of being unconventional. You should feel free to defy convention. Often, I see people on the verge of thrilling positive change. Then, suddenly, the cold, iron grip of the status quo clenches, obliterating opportunity, freedom, and authentic need.

Even though excitement boils for the possibility of change, be it a fresh job, a new home, or a fledgling relationship, there's an inner critic who's attached to your present reality. It's that little voice who whispers that you're comfortable with your inertia and trajectory. This can make you question a new opportunity and stifle or undermine progress.

Instead of feeling a sense of happy anticipation about

the prospect of change, you might feel immobilized by a flurry of fears and anxieties. This fear drives conformity to conventional beliefs, ideologies, and practices. By conforming, your ability to think outside the box, break generational maladies, and discover progression is hampered. It tells you to *"get back in your box"* and enquires, *"Who do you think you are?"*

Ask yourself, *Do you really wish to be a follower?*

Do you wish to walk with the rest of the crowd or dare to stand out?

Often, adopting unconventional ways can be positive rather than negative. For example, instead of applying for a 9-5 job, which pays an average salary, you might establish your own business. It may be difficult. Multiple resources will be required for its birth. But it may prove infinitely more fruitful and fulfilling. Learn to thank your fears, then walk straight past them.

Step Four – Showing Self-compassion

I cannot stress this enough; be kinder to yourself. If

you become caught up in the endless cycle of pleasing others, you neither serve yourself nor them. You don't leave sufficient time or energy to express self-compassion. Kindness can fly out the window.

Being kind to yourself provides space to breathe. By surrendering the art of being self-critical, you free yourself. With this step, you can swap that low-grade, gnawing feeling for one of lightness and control.

Do you ever call yourself names like 'stupid' or 'loser?'

Do you ever repetitively berate yourself for your mistakes?

Have you ever pushed your body and mind so far past the point of being tired and hungry that you almost collapse in a heap?

If so, it's time to stop, to free your mind from negativity. Instead, engage in positive, uplifting conversations with yourself. Take note of how far you've come, how good you're doing in your life, the numerous goals you've already achieved. There is much to discuss!

We all have moments of pain and distress when the demands of our lives are so challenging that they stretch us to our limits. We struggle and fight against our feelings, almost like drowning in quicksand. This is when we need to extend kindness toward ourselves the most. It's called self-compassion.

Step Five – Be Okay with Saying No

Learn to say no. This single step could change your life! Saying *No* allows you to take charge, stand up for yourself, and hold your unique course. If you continue to say *Yes,* even when you don't want to, your resentment and regret will grow. You will also set a new precedent; *'yes'* will become the default expectation.

Saying *No* does not mean you are selfish, rude, or unkind. These are unhelpful beliefs that make a polite refusal difficult. At times, it's imperative to be direct. Do not apologize for being so. Remember that it is better to decline now than be resentful later. A *'no'* can be delivered with politeness and calm; your *'no'* need not be aggressive (unless warranted).

If you're still not comfortable, practice. Imagine a scenario and then practice saying *No* either by yourself or with a friend or family member. If this feels too confronting, remember that visualization is a powerful tool to wire new pathways in your brain. Over time, you will become comfortable uttering this atomic word. You'll feel empowered and gain the freedom you desire.

Step Six – Learn to Set Boundaries

Learning to set crystal clear, firm boundaries both professionally and in your personal life will protect you from toxic behavior.

What are boundaries? They're not threats or ultimatums; they're set limits that others should not cross. Boundaries form guidelines. They tell others how to treat you and define the behaviors you expect.

Setting boundaries is essential. They provide a protective buffer from emotional and physical pain, be it in the workplace, amongst peers, family members, friends, or others. Boundaries are often necessary to protect your time, your space, and your feelings.

Don't allow others to take advantage of your kindness and generosity. Self-awareness informs how and where you set your boundaries. You must be aware and honest with your feelings, needs, and expectations.

Inform others clearly and directly. Explain respectfully and honestly what you find offensive or unacceptable. Be specific. Start with the easiest boundaries first.

Setting boundaries is a skill that needs to be cultivated. Enlist support from others, if necessary. Immediately inform people when they have crossed the line. Don't wait. Communicate politely and directly. Be clear about the consequences and then follow through.

Remember, establishing boundaries is your right; you are undoubtedly entitled to respect. While you can't control how another person chooses to behave, you do have control over the lines you draw and how you allow people to treat you.

Step Seven – Embrace Learning

Make a habit of engaging novelty and embrace what

life teaches you. Instead of sticking to the same items, routines and hobbies, opt for different.

Many opportunities are lost to fear or habit. But when you try something fresh, it may be amazing for you! You may even find some undiscovered, hidden potential or talent.

So, go on adventures with your friends and family, change your wardrobe, express *your* personal style instead of following fashion trends, enjoy foods from outside your native cuisine, seek better or more diverse employment opportunities. Live!

Step Eight – Step Out of Your Comfort Zone

As the popular and accurate saying goes: *"Success lies on the other side of your comfort zone."*

Try your level best to reinforce and implement this saying in your daily life. Encourage yourself to step out of your comfort zone. It has constricted you for so long.

Keep in mind that change begins with you — no one can be your voice. No two people think exactly the same. You possess a uniqueness which means your comfort zone is unique, too. Your challenge depends on where *your* boundaries lay. Consider, also, that your initial strides can be small.

Time doesn't wait for anyone to awaken from their deep slumber; it passes in the blinking of an eye. This is why now is the time to act, to take full control of your life. In the process of doing so, you will shine a vital light that helps others to snap out of their illusion and forge a path of their own.

Ask yourself, if not now, when? Tomorrow is never guaranteed.

Chapter 4

Other Lessons for a Healthy, Happy & Well-lived Life

"You cannot medicate yourself out of a problem you be-haved yourself into."

- Dr. Lindsey

While there are billions of people alive on our planet, have you ever asked yourself how many lead effervescent, fulfilling lives? A life permeated with utmost happiness, satisfaction, and contentedness? One built by cultivating the daily habits that lead to joy? Just think about it.

How amazing would it be to hop out of bed each and every morning, feeling excited and purposeful about your day?

*How satisfying would it be to go to bed every night
with a smile of immense satisfaction on your lips and a mind
at peace?*

This may seem unachievable but living a fulfilling
life is possible for you, too. Like many others, I've felt the
rollercoaster ride of emotions that accompany life's highs
and lows. Clearly, life isn't always easy. Yet, through conscious and deliberate action and intent, I live a life filled with
inspiration, balance, boundaries, and fulfillment. I attest to
this possibility for you.

Life is often accompanied by an array of challenges,
defeats, and failures. But through it all, no matter what is
happening, there are always ways to feel more fulfilled.
What's more, they don't require much effort!

If you look deep within yourself, you'll soon realize
and humbly acknowledge that you, along with others, have
aspects that drag you down. Pieces that do not serve you.
Parts that hold you back from the life you wish to live. Let
these go.

*How do you become unstuck from things, places, and
people that no longer serve you and then move forward with*

crystal clear direction?

The first step is to gain self-awareness and define your current reality. This will help you see why you continue to hit the same wall over and again. Once you understand what that is and where you are, you can start breaking free instantly.

The second is to build up mental and emotional armor in order to safeguard you on your journey to the fulfilling life you aspire to.

The third? This chapter will show you how to focus on daily activities that move the needle, which translates into a more fulfilled life. What's important to remember is that it all begins and ends with what *you choose* daily and the impact your choices make. There are several activities that, if practiced regularly, will result in a higher quality of life.

Factors That Help You to Live a More Fulfilled Life

"I believe that the greatest gift you can give your family and this world is a healthy you,"

- Joyce Meyer

The wonder about the daily activities I'm about to share is that they're fairly common. In fact, you might even indulge already. Let's see...

Healthy Cooking

For starters, let's talk about how to optimize your health through your diet. That means every morsel you consume, your complete eating habits. It's no secret that you are what you eat. So, ensure your diet is not only delicious but nutritious and sufficiently healthy to fuel your body and brain.

Cooking is a common activity that most people, both women, and men, enjoy. Preparing your own food makes it simpler to eat healthily. It allows you to slow down. It encourages a deeper connection with the food you consume. Proper home-cooked meals are fantastic opportunities to nourish yourself as well as fill your stomach.

Preparing food is fulfilling in and of itself. However, it requires the allocation of time and effort for ourselves and rewards one for doing so. Sitting down to a hot meal you've personally prepared can make mealtime more enjoyable and fulfilling.

To cook is also an adventure. By trying new spices, ingredients, recipes, and tastes, you get to experience a glimpse at a different culture. If you lack time to cook every day, carve out space in your schedule for designated days and batch cook. Taking homemade leftovers for the following day's lunch will extend the joy of a home-cooked, fresh meal wherever you go.

What diet should you choose? Inflammation is the hallmark of all diseases, and my personal recommendation is to enjoy an anti-inflammatory diet. Head over to Deflame for more information on how to remove pro-inflammatory foods from your diet. Inflammatory foods can differ from person to person. For example, eating too many grains, fried foods, or even peanuts can cause issues for a person.

The good news is that to counter the situation, all you

need to do is increase foods that contain Omega-3 acids such as oily fish- salmon, sardines, and anchovies or vegan sources walnuts, chia, and flaxseed. Importantly, you must also add anti-inflammatory herbs and spices, such as *cumin, turmeric, ginger, garlic, oregano, Boswellia, rosemary, bromelain, thyme, cloves, cinnamon,* and *cayenne pepper powder.*

These are potent anti-inflammatories and should be included to achieve homeostasis — biological balance — within and for your body.

Your Work-life Routine

Work is fundamental to society and so our sense of self. However, for many, there is a chasmic imbalance between it and non-work life. It's taking its toll. A job provides money to support our families and us. Unfortunately, many people believe that's its sole function. It's common to meet people who are stuck pursuing an occupation they dislike, even loathe, in search of status, to fulfill the expectations of others, or because it pays well. But...

At some point in our lives, most of us ask, "*Is this it? Was I just put on this planet to pay bills, work long hours, and never have enough time to have some fun?"*

If you have ever felt that the opportunity to live a more fulfilling life was passing you by, you're not alone. Maybe surprisingly, your job can play a role in regaining your vitality. See, your professional role can provide more than monetary gains alone. Your job becomes an intrinsic part of your life, so if the rewards are shallow and you pine for depth, work becomes a burden. Lack of fulfillment in the career space is draining. Promotions, new assignments, and pay rises, while welcome, are insufficient.

To rub salaried salt into the wound, promotions may require longer work hours that eat into precious time with your family and leave little room for recreational activities. Not to mention, the sedentary nature of many positions harms your spine and hinders your nervous systems and wellbeing. Too much time spent sitting contributes to back stiffness and pain. It stresses the spinal discs and muscles, particularly in your back and neck. It leads to deconditioning, loss of fitness and physique and can leave you feeling wired.

So, when I hear statements like, *"Once I get the promotion, raise, car, house, goal weight, etc., I'll be happy,"* I inwardly cringe. This mindset couldn't be farther from the truth and, at its worst, prevents us from living our lives to the fullest. A focus on creating a fulfilling, happier career is wiser. Interestingly, this will amp up your productivity, enhance the quality of your work, and create professional alchemy.

Does this sound too good to be true?

I kid you not; fulfillment and satisfaction are key components to a successful career. An optimistic outlook increases performance and accomplishment, which creates a virtuous career cycle. In addition to this, cognitive function is heightened by a positive mindset and only a healthy dose of stress.

When we feel optimistic about the future, our focus becomes laser pointed; we regain our innate energy and transform into infinitely better problem solvers. Nature truly has an in-built compass, guiding each one of us to a happier tomorrow.

Remember that living a meaningful and fulfilling life extends beyond monetary gains. Consciously choosing inspired thought and action provides a center point and path to blossom into the most wholesome version of ourselves. This allows us to show up fully at work, at home, and in the community.

It's never too late to create the career you desire. You have the potency required to alter and manifest your destiny.

Movement and Meditation

While these two practices continue to grow in popularity, they are not standard daily practices within America. I believe they should be. The benefits are both meaningful and extensive. Their practice doesn't require tiresome hour-long sessions, Bootcamp regimes, or a Zen clearing of your mind...

Being physically active might mean a 10-minute walk, a yoga class, a set of stretches, or a passionate dancing sesh. A swim on the beach, a wilderness hike, skipping rope, or an aqua-aerobics class. What you choose can be as unique as you are. Find an exercise that you love; that way, it'll feel filled with ease and magic rather than become a chore. All that matters is you move your body regularly. Even 20-minutes, three times per week, will make a significant difference.

Meditation is simple, yet its practice brings a host of benefits and blessings. It acts like a balm for mental health to reduce stress, ease depression, and calm anxiety. Pain relief, improved sleep, lower blood pressure, better focus, enhanced memory, peace, and serenity are often reported. If working out exercises your body, meditation exercises your mind.

Many people think meditation is sitting still, in a state free from all thought. This may be a goal for monk levels mastery. However, it is not required. The aim, at its core, is to observe thoughts or feelings as they arise. Then let them go; do not cling. With ease, bring yourself back to the present moment.

If meditation does not feel comfortable at first, know this is entirely normal. Simply persist; you are doing a great job. Every skill takes time to develop.

You may find comfort by using a guided mediation that prompts you along the way. There are apps to support you. I recommend *Insight timer,* which is free, and *Calm,* a paid app and personal favorite. I tried meditation without feeling successful in my practice for years. I am now hooked! Meditation is essential to my health and wellbeing.

What's more, I believe children should learn meditation at a young age, so they develop a healthy way to cope with life's inevitable ups and downs. This will amplify peace and calm. As the Dalai Lama said, *"If every eight-year-old in the world is taught meditation, we will eliminate violence from the world in one generation."*

Breathwork — a focus on intentionally changing the breath — combined with meditation further enhances the benefits. This combination provides an excellent way to manage stress, wind down at the end of the day, and open the perfect space for gratitude.

Hushing Your Inner Critic

Most of us have a lurking inner critic hidden within ourselves. Your inner critic allows destructive, degrading thoughts to enter your mind and run wild with demeaning self-talk. It is important to apply the **RAIN** acronym and discern between your inner critic and your conscience. One can tell the difference by how they make you feel.

Your inner critic will be self-defeating/self-destructive thoughts, i.e., *"I'm not good enough," "You'll never be successful,"* or *"I'm stupid."* It makes you feel unworthy and shameful. On the other hand, your conscience is trust-worthy and motivates us to change undesirable actions con-structively. i.e., *"I can do hard things," "I am prepared to overcome any challenge,"* or *"I handle setbacks grace-fully."* When your inner critic shows up, I find it helpful to name it; maybe use the name of a bully from school, or go with the ubiquitous *"Karen"* reference.

Literally, tell yourself, *"Oh, here comes Neagrive Nancy rearing her ugly head."* Observe what the inner critic is saying, and remember you don't have to assimilate the thought into your person. Notice it and allow it to pass, re-placing it with something aligned with your unlimited, gor-geous, strong, authentic self.

Healthy Socializing

We, humans, are social creatures. We all wish to be loved and to belong. Therefore, spending sufficient leisure time with like-minded and bonded souls is restorative.

Healthy socializing can provide recreation, remove your attention from your stressors, and enable personal in-teraction. You might experience eager anticipation for known or new people and events. It presents the opportunity to learn new skills and information; to expand your mind.

Longing for greater fulfillment is common. As we live, we evolve, enter new chapters, seek greater depths, or simply wish for change. To alter life in a meaningful way, we must decide what we want and set daily goals to move closer.

Focusing on the activities discussed above will most certainly create transformation. The best part is unachievable time commitment is not required. An hour a day will suffice. Take it one day at a time and begin now. You have everything required to create a life that is complete with happiness, fulfillment, and abundance. And you deserve it!

Consistently taking small yet deliberate actions that compound on one another is powerful. This effect can dramatically and positively alter the course of your life in unimaginable and joyful ways!

Creating the Life That You Want

We all aspire to *do* great, *be* great, and accrue material wealth. In short, to build a great life. Yet, most of us haven't created the successful life of our dreams. We constantly complain that we don't have enough money, success, romance, or joy. We point fingers and blame external factors; *"if that"* hadn't happened to me, *"if only"* life was fair, *"if this"* wasn't making life difficult.

But what we need to understand and always remember is that greatness exists in *all* of us. Yes, this includes *you!* Regardless of personal circumstances, fewer resources, challenging economic times, or other perceived impediments, you must maintain faith. You are more powerful than you can imagine. We can each create the life we desire.

To conceive and manifest the life of your dreams, you must uncover the core desire to do so and learn how to harness its potential. I highly recommend reading Danielle LaPorte's, *The Desire Map* to focus on directing your actions to accomplish your heart's goals.

While a perfect life is an unachievable enigma, there are many ways to improve your life each and every day. And if you feel as though you've trodden down a wayward path? So long as there is air in your lungs, you change your footfall and walk a new path—step by step. The journey starts with you. No one else can tread your life for you. Neither can nor should they create for you the life you desire.

It's *you* who remains in charge of your destiny, just as it should be. Don't let fear get blind or bind you. In truth, there is no certainty in life. Do not become complacent because you are comfortable, especially when your intuition whispers, *"There is something better. Reach for it. Honor your inner wisdom."*

Steps to Better Your Life

Are you unsure how to take the next steps to better your life? Or how to re-find the long-lost track to a fulfilled and positive life. Here are five steps I recommend:

Step One – Know What You Want

The first step seems obvious once spoken: decide what you want. It sounds simple, but being overly busy, unsatisfied, and physically and spiritually drained can dim the light of inspiration and awareness. It's time to slow down and gift yourself time to prioritize your life. You must create a clear map for what you want, then take steps to get there.

After your desires have been clearly defined, ask yourself what success looks like to you (everyone's definition is different). My definition of success is waking up each day doing exactly what I want to do because I control my life.

Stamp out your inner devil's advocate and that incessant to-do list as they will inhibit you from dreaming authentically or big if this is your aspiration. As soon as you commit fully to a lofty dream and chase it, boots and all, your subconscious mind will discover creative ideas to draw it into your reality. Then, you'll start attracting the right people, the ideal opportunities, and the perfect resources to transform your desired fiction into fact.

It's essential to identify what you want, those habits and beliefs you need to change, and how you imagine your life blossoming into the beautiful one from your dreams. Then, by deciding, you can focus strongly on the promises you are making to yourself.

Tip: Towering dreams will compel you. They'll also inspire others to aim for the same.

Step Two – Becoming Goal-oriented

The second step is to become goal-oriented and unleash the power of your innate drive. The brain is a goal-seeking, problem-solving organism. Whatever goal you give your subconscious mind, it will toil day and night to achieve it. Remember that self-motivated people succeed because they push themselves to step outside of the ordinary, learn new skills, and accomplish their goals.

This is the time — this very moment — to invest in yourself. To gift yourself time to figure out what you want from life and then take steps to achieve it. As a matter of fact, even just thinking about your goals can help you complete them faster because contemplation stirs your mind into action. Just don't become trapped in the thinking process!

To get started, establish your goals and visualize having already achieved them. Then, fully immerse yourself in this scenario. Feel, see, hear, taste, and smell what's around you in your mind's eye. Combine visualization with mediation or positive affirmations. These processes help you imagine yourself in your new lifestyle, rewiring your brain along the way. This allows you to gradually step into a changed reality, one where your outer and inner views will soon match.

Step Three – Believe in Yourself

The third step is to believe in yourself.

If you don't, then how will others believe in you?

To create and sustain the life of your dreams, you must believe you are indeed capable of making it happen. Whether you call it self-esteem, self-assurance, or self-confidence, it's a deep-seated belief that you have what it takes - that you hold the necessary abilities, talents, and skills to create your desired results. You must have unwavering faith in yourself to prosper through both the good and bad.

Make the conscious choice to believe that you create *all* your experiences. Your successes, as well as the pain, struggle, and strife, all come from you. It may sound strange, but accepting this level of responsibility is exceptionally empowering.

It means you can *do*, *change*, and *be* anything YOU want.

Step Four – Overcoming Your Fears

Next is the courageous step of surrendering fear. Fearfulness will only serve as a barrier for you. It will hold you back and stop you from achieving your dreams. The fear of making a mistake is natural, but the only way you can know if a choice is right or wrong for you is by simply making a decision; to begin. If you ever feel frightened about the changes you are making, try to place an anchor in your mind or space. A virtual or physical tether to remind you of your goals and your why. It might be a person, a mission statement, or an object. Return to this anchor to keep yourself focused on your improved life.

Moreover, take full responsibility for your life. None of us are entitled to a great life. No one else has the responsibility to give us a wonderful life simply because we exist. The real truth is there's only one person responsible for your quality of life: you. Your experience results from your actions: your income, relationships, health (to a surprisingly large extent), debt, fitness level, attitudes, behaviors, and more. The person who is reflected back to you as you stand in front of the mirror is the chief conductor of your life.

I feel everyone knows this in their heart of hearts, but the mind can play games. We can fall into the trap of believing external factors are the source of failure, unhappiness, and disappointment. But the truth of the matter is that external factors don't always determine how you live. You are in complete control of the quality of your life. The sooner you realize and accept this, the more empowered you will become.

Successful people take full responsibility for their thoughts, the images they visualize, and the actions they take. They don't waste their time and energy blaming and complaining. They take accountability for their actions without judging themselves harshly. Instead, they evaluate their experiences and decide if they need to implement change or not. In the face of discomfort, they take calculated risks and don't stop.

Step Five – Do What Makes You Happy

The last step may seem counterintuitive but is essential; do more of what makes you happy. When working out how to create the life you desire, consider experiences that truly make you happy. Do them as often as possible.

Prioritizing pleasure, fun and laughter are indispensable aids in this crazy ride we call life. You were put on the Earth, at this time, to live your truth. Therefore, waking up each day eager and inspired, joyful, and happy is a blessing. At its core, this is likely why you wish to transform your life.

For some, that might mean working toward their dreams. For others, it could mean playing with their children or writing in their journals more frequently. However you wish your life to be, make sure you repeat these affirmative actions to create a positive and happy life.

To conclude, instead of conforming to society, it's time we stood up. We each must become active players in our own lives. You deserve to lead the life you desire. The inspiring and terrifying truth is the ball is in your court; it's up to you. You only get one life. It's both your right and responsibility to live it fully.

Making Changes That Will Honor Your-self

Honoring yourself is the practice of respecting your mind, body, and soul by immersion in practices that benefit you. It's allowing yourself to align with your goals to pave the way to a healthier, happier life. It's permitting yourself to go after your desires!

How can you act to honor yourself and live a better life? Let's take a look...

Proper Sleep Routine

While we live in a society that pushes us to *do* more, *be* more, *give* more, and *have* more, we must take time to re-charge.

Stop scrolling, reading, shopping, doing, and devote time to sufficient restful sleep. Heading to bed earlier provides time to process the day's changes and challenges and detoxify your tissues.

Sound sleep is fundamental to your overall health for a multitude of reasons. In the short term, poor sleep can affect your mood, judgment, and ability to retain information.

As JoJo Jensen said, *"Without enough sleep, we all become tall two-year-olds."* In the long term, chronic sleep deprivation can lead to cardiovascular disease, diabetes, obesity, and early death.

Sleep ergonomics is a key component that is often overlooked. The best sleep position is on the back with a supportive pillow under the neck (not the base of the head). This supports the natural forward curve of the cervical spine.

Healthy Nutrition

As the saying goes, *"You are what you eat."* A diet that consists of optimal nutrition establishes and maintains the foundation for good health. If, on the other hand, you fuel your body with junk, you're holding yourself back from living a fulfilling life. Rubbish in, rubbish out, as they say.

Opt for nutrient-dense foods. Drink water that is alkaline and pure—practice mindfulness when eating instead of scattering your attention on inefficient multitasking or work. Eat well to live better.

Whatever size you may be, when you eat nutritious food, move your body regularly, drink uncontaminated water, and talk kindly to yourself, you are the size you're meant to be. Do not judge yourself by the number on a scale, your pant size, or the number of likes on social media. You are more than a number.

You are a highly intelligent, beautiful soul inside a flesh-form designed to carry you through this life; a human incarnation on a spinning rock in the incredible universe. I repeat, do not let numbers define your self-worth!

Journaling

Journaling is considered to be one of the pre-eminent life-changing habits. Many famous creatives, innovators, writers, and original thinkers of our generation keep and maintain journals. I consider it a creative necessity, a place for self-analysis, exploration, and for some, a form of art. Practice journaling to help you prioritize, clarify your thinking, and accomplish your most important tasks.

Regular Exercise

Exercise is one part of the daily routine that many people love to hate. It's easy to find tons of excuses not to move. However, exercise is one of the greatest gifts you can give yourself and your life. Not only will consistent physical activity power your fitness, but you'll also notice that you feel lighter and happier.

Meditation

Meditation is a simple way to breathe, detox, relax, and surrender tension and stress from your heart and mind. Thus, meditate often. Schedule at least ten minutes into your everyday routine for this empowering and grounding practice.

Meditation, especially when performed when you wake in the morning, is a great way to begin your day.

Minimizing Your Screen Time

The world we live in is a sphere of technology; various fascinating gadgets capture and hold our attention and time. We spend countless hours staring at computers, phones, and television with little consideration for the consequences. Medical doctor Robert Lustig's eye-opening book, *The Hacking of the American Mind*, describes how cellphone use is linked to increased stress, sleep loss, and depression.

Minimizing your screen time is beneficial in a number of ways. For me, one of the most important is the time it frees up. When you give less time to the screen, you can spend more time interacting with those around you—more time grounding yourself in nature and more time immersed in your life. Contentment can be realized as tech is swapped for life.

Reading

Reading is an excellent way to grow as an individual and find meaning in your life. Reading makes it possible to learn new skills and insight, become more aware, be intellectually stimulated, and gain new perspectives. Make reading a habit, and you'll soon discover how the written word can change your life for the better.

As with any advice, you will only benefit when you implement it. Will you focus only on the theory or act? Are you ready to transform your life? In the end, it's always up to you.

Start now and take the consistent steps forward, no matter how small. For example, if you add one wellness practice for each of the next twelve months, you will have developed one dozen new self-care habits one year from now. The results will be palpable, allowing you to show up as your highest self.

Imagine how you'll feel if you dedicate your next twelve months to:

1. Meditation

2. Affirmations

3. Mindful living

4. Setting boundaries

5. Future visualization

6. Journaling, writing

7. Transformational breathing

8. Reading enriching books

9. Staying in the present moment

10. Stretching

11. Hydrating

12. Nourishing your body through nutrient-dense foods

Rather, rise above these conditioned behaviors and know that your dreams and actions create your reality. It's now or never, and this is your call—remember that.

So, now that you've read this entire chapter, tell me;

Are you motivated enough to live your life to the fullest?

Chapter 5

Change is About …

"You can't go back and change the beginning, but you can start where you are and change the ending."

- C.S. Lewis

The concept of change can be quite unsettling. We are often taught to fear it, so naturally, we slowly acquire a dislike for it. Sometimes, change can herald devastating moments. Unfortunately, many of us simply prefer to shy away from further change, no matter how big or small. As the saying goes, *"Better the devil, you know."*

However, change is an integral part of your personal development journey and, for the most part, needs to be embraced. Actively striving for affirming personal metamorphosis will transform your life. Otherwise, there will be absolutely no growth; you'll remain static and stuck. Yet, change can be embraced without sudden dramatic shifts.

A focus on kindling the capacity for acceptance and adaptability toward change is a wonderful starting point. See, nothing remains stagnant. Change affects all aspects of our lives and circumstances. It is unavoidable, and refusal only leads to further suffering. On the other hand, being willing and able to adapt brings tranquility and provides a smoother, more enjoyable path through life.

Understanding Resistance to Change

Two important questions to ponder are, *Why do we display such a resistance to change?*

What is the connection to social conformity?

For many, the basic instinct is to try their level best to ensure methods, traditions, and practices remain constant and conform to existing social patterns and customs. Even those who are a little flexible do not necessarily like to accept change in the existing social system. Understanding the reasons behind this is a good idea that begs the question: Why do people resist change?

Loss of Old Connections

People are conditioned to follow specific patterns

and maintain a certain orderliness in their daily lifestyles. Above all, we are creatures of habit. We feel happiest when we stick to routines, adhere to our own timetables, and follow certain rules and regulations that define our norms and standards. They offer us a source of comfort. Any change can cause resentment and raise the fear of losing established connections, expectations, and conventions.

Constant Insecurity

Fear of change can be due to constant insecurity. Change can frighten, particularly for those who have experienced much insecurity and at times when they were unprepared. Life doesn't always warn us when sudden change is imminent, so the experience can be stressful, even traumatic, for some.

Uncertainty about the impact of change can be extremely difficult to deal with. Loss of job and future security or of emotional or physical wellbeing takes a toll. New technology, new systems, new procedures can all create uncertainty and, hence, resistance to change. People often only start taking active steps toward the unknown if they genuinely believe and accept that the risks of standing still are greater than those of moving in a new direction.

The Emotional Turmoil

One of the chief reasons for resistance centers on the emotional turmoil that a change may cause, especially if past experiences have not been positive or favorable. This results in a lack of trust and stubbornness so that even when change is well-intended and designed, its significance is misinterpreted, leading to resistance.

This is why it is necessary to be flexible. Whenever a change in the existing social system becomes imperative and unavoidable, people with a flexible, dynamic mind and mindset tend to adapt well. No social tradition, societal norm, system value, custom, order, or cultural heritage is indelibly permanent. Their change either happens slowly or suddenly.

Hence, developing flexible and open attributes empower ease in embracing change. To help lighten your load, remind yourself that it couldn't have happened any other way.

The Drawbacks of Conforming to Social Norms

Various sociologists believe that man, being a social creature, aims to conform to the social system that it creates. Conformity is a type of social influence that dictates the behavior or beliefs of an individual so that they can fit in with a particular group.

Compliance happens as a response to either real or perceived expectations or peer pressure from within the group. It may also involve the pressure of societal norms or a general aspiration to achieve a specific level of success.

In the present society, the word *"conformity"* is mainstream and dictates every aspect of our lives. Consequently, conformity to social norms is present in everything we do.

However, while in the animal kingdom, social conformity can be the difference between life and death, conformity is not entirely beneficial for humans. There can be harmful, soul-sucking drawbacks to conforming to social norms.

You are *Following* a Career Path

Choosing a career is one of the major and highly important decisions in one's life. Unfortunately, very few people in this world *choose* their ideal career because they are passionate about it. On the other hand, there's a large number of people who are *following* a career.

Think about it. *How many people do you know who begin or follow careers they have no interest in or actively dislike because they succumb to the pressure of what is advised, expected, and considered fruitful?*

Many people are stuck in mind-numbing, soul-crushing careers because they've been gradually persuaded, manipulated to believe that *"Passion does not put food on the table."* It is deeply impressed upon us that we should be happy with an amazing paycheck, fringe benefits, and appreciation from family and friends… All that is required is to be dead inside.

The fear of pitfalls often dissuades those who consider following their dreams and passions. They won't enjoy a nice house, a prestigious car, or even find a loving spouse. In this light, social conformity is stifling, isn't it?

Opting For Comfort Over Adventure

It's no surprise that most people love to be comfortable. It's one of the defining aspects behind concepts like *Cottage core* or *Hygge* – the Danish practice of enjoying comfort, coziness, and contentment in every little thing.

Most prefer a life cushioned by comfort and convenience. The fear of surrendering comfort can hover overhead like a dark grey cloud. So many times, comfort is chosen instead of adventure. But this extracts a cost; it hampers personal progress and true happiness.

The downside of opting for a comfortable, convenient life over one of adventure is that the golden opportunities, those once-in-a-lifetime chances, are readily ignored. This can result in a manmade prison. You can become trapped in your comfort zone. And once you've become embedded, enmeshed, in your habits, breaking free from the indoctrination of social norms becomes difficult.

Comfort can kill the adventurous spirit that awaits inside, desperate for release. Material ease acts to anesthetize the whispers. To place the bricks that subconsciously build a wall of fear, discovering the other side of the comfort zone is nearly impossible.

Those that wish to explore simply cannot find the courage or the clarity due to conformity and servitude to social norms. An example of choosing comfort over adventure is seen in how we live. The norm states we should live in a house or be a part of a community. So you buy or rent to blend in. In reality, you could live wherever you wish. Be it a tiny houseboat, a converted bus, a hay-bale house, even a decked-out ice-cream truck.

One of my favorite quotes is from a poem by Robert Frost, which says:

"Two roads diverged in a wood, and I— I took the one less traveled by, And that has made all the difference."

What path will lead you down the most wonderful, contented, mind-blowing journey?

Worrying Excessively About Your Appearance

We live in a highly critical society, one that sets unattainable goals and then punishes perceived imperfections. At some point in our lives, most of us have felt concerned about our personal appearance. This may be fleeting, striking when confidence is low. For others, it's a permanent worry. Much time is spent pre-occupied by the niggling notion of being physically unattractive, not sufficiently pretty or handsome, not fit or good enough.

Artificially constructed, unrealistic beauty and fitness standards extract a hefty toll. Preteens, teenagers, adults, and even the elderly have become focused on and conscious about appearance. This creates a constant worry about what others think of you: *What opinions are being voiced? What thoughts are being told?* This sabotages confidence and halts self-care.

When we worry that we don't fit society's standards, we, oftentimes, go to mad lengths just to fit in. To be accepted. It is important to remember that the standard of beauty is ever-changing. If you base your worth on current beauty ideals, you will always feel less than.

The corporate push to breed self-hate serves a capital agenda. When you feel insecure, your desire to purchase products that may fill the void or deliver short-term relief can be ravenous—Fat-phobic, wrinkle-phobic, youth-focused sells.

Instead, focus on what you love about yourself. Journal your positive traits and features. What do you love about yourself when you feel in your authentic power? Then, if and when you have a low self-esteem day (and you likely will), you can refer back to what a badass human being you are! Remind yourself of all the wonderful ways being you is beautiful. (This list could and should include more than just how good your butt looks in those pants!)

Forming Inauthentic Friendships

The misleading social norm that states friendships serve as a function for ambition is that inauthenticity to get ahead is acceptable and is deeply troubling. In a dog-eat-dog world, friends are sometimes viewed as merely a path to gain access to the desired outcome, climb the social and economic ladder, and be seen as more than.

There is also the expectation that you have a sufficient number of friends, lest you be an outcast. So you scramble to form friendships without worrying about who they are and what they think of you. In reality, it doesn't matter how many friends you do or don't have. You may prefer to exist in a large community of people or lead a solitary lifestyle. What matters is that you're happy and your re-lationships are genuine.

Inauthentic friendships don't last long or matter much. They deliver loneliness, lack of companionship, and a scarcity of trust. When founded on insincerity, a friendship is doomed from the start. Friends should support you, encourage you, and love you. Never settle for less. Know your worth. Establish how you should be treated and hold a high standard. And if you are no longer being served by a friend-ship (or any relationship for that matter), feel free to distance yourself. Ensure you prioritize your happiness.

Increases the Chances of Depression

Most people face the terror of social rejection at some point during their lives. Unfortunately, the experience of rejection can trigger you to conform to the status quo, even if it does not sit right with your authentic self. This can create a people-pleasing persona, social anxiety, and an insipid, lingering fear that eats away at your confidence. The concern? That others will judge you and find you lacking.

For some, social anxiety is so strong that it induces

panic attacks. This can trigger self-isolation and the development of a severe anxiety disorder like agoraphobia. This can be ruinous for mental health and contribute to the development of depression.

Loss of Identity

Each one of us is uniquely different from another. We each have our own character, personality traits, behaviors, and habits and react according to these. Yet, applied social pressure, expectations, and actions to ensure conformity may force a loss of personal identity. The moment you express an opinion that doesn't jive with the majority-held belief, there's a good chance influence will be exerted to change your mind. To bring you back to the fray.

But, if you behave in a way that is contrary to your value systems just to fit in, you will slowly and surely erase your individuality. Through neuroplasticity, you will alter the connections within your brain until you lose track of who you are. Your inner compass then becomes hidden. Until you find, as the saying goes, *"When you stand for nothing, you fall for everything."*

Leads to Dependence

A loss of identity can create co-dependence especially when you base your worth on what others think. That is when confusion sets in. Questions like, *What do I want?* and *What should I do?* become difficult to answer. You begin to think less about yourself and more in terms of what others want from you. When you conform in this way, you give them control over you. You relinquish your power.

This process often occurs without the conscious knowledge of the other person. Although it can be helpful to receive input and support from others, you must consider independent thought and action. Blindly and carelessly handing over your agency only benefits those who receive it.

Conformity, from this perspective, is abjectly harmful. It's time that we change the notion that crippling, objectionable social norms ought to be followed. Instead, instill and reinforce the notion that being independent *and* supportive is what society needs to function harmoniously. As we wisen, we will realize that giving should be balanced with receiving. If all you do is give, receiving nothing in return, it's time to walk away.

Why We Conform to Social Norms

It's well-established that people tend to conform to common behaviors within their communities. These are known as social norms. So, '*Why do people prefer to choose what others think and do?*'

The reason for this branches into two main aspects.

The first reason is that some social norms are rational and beneficial. Following and conforming to those norms make it easier and safer to live life. For instance, the social norm of clothing your body, grooming yourself, and being polite to others fosters connection and ease without harm.

The second reason is due to the pressure and expectations of people within a society. To put it simply, people who follow norms are rewarded, whereas people who don't may be punished. Sometimes, individuals only co-operate with certain social norms for fear of the consequences of not conforming. An example is a young girl dieting and exercising so that she can be deemed attractive. Why? The current stereotypical norm states that thin women are more appealing.

Social norms, both good or bad, arise in every culture. It is up to each of us to decide if we wish *if we should* follow them. Remember: It is only when we stand up for our innermost truths that the potential for transformation is birthed. So, the next time you feel pressured to act or be a certain way, gift yourself a few minutes to think and feel. *Is this right for you?*

By embracing and accepting your authentic self, you will reach a conclusion steeped in self-love and intelligence. Opt for what makes you happy and ignore what others may think. As long as you feel happy and proud of yourself, it doesn't matter what other people think. Live your life to please yourself and not others.

Taking a Look at the Cascade Effect

The cascade effect is a sequence of events in which each event produces the circumstances required to initiate the next one. The following is an example that explains this phenomenon.

When you see a packed restaurant next to an empty one, you automatically assume that the packed restaurant's food is better, right? Suppose everyone else follows the same thought process (most will). In this case, it's possible that restaurant-goers entered the first restaurant without due consideration for the menu, the cleanliness, the quality, or the ethics. The full restaurant was seen as being popular and so attracted a hearty crowd.

The second remained empty because of preconception rather than knowledge or experience. In this way, social norms can quickly snowball. Significant can flourish simply based on other people's decisions. The more deeply we understand why people conform to social norms, the easier it becomes to design behavioral interventions to address the problems facing our society... And, on a personal level, to open our eyes and step into a richer, rewarding life.

The Importance of Fostering Change to Live the Life You Desire

What is crucial to realize is that change is essential, and it all begins with YOU! Change the way you think and act, and you will inadvertently and powerfully change the way you live. It's time to raise your voice and take a stand for yourself. To live the unfettered life of your dreams, you must start to make the most of this life and live it how you want. Of course, some past experiences and teachings influence how you behave, react, and conform. These can be surrendered. So, consider this your wake-up call.

You were put on this Earth to achieve a purpose. To enjoy and learn while serving your community in whatever capacity you feel passionate about. Do not let archaic social norms dominate your life and dampen your lived experience. Break the cycle and do so courageously!

Start by culling norms that hold you back from living the life you truly desire. Reevaluate what works for you and what doesn't. Let the latter go. Allot time to ponder things realistically. Then make suitable choices that cater to your needs. Sometimes, the harsh truth is that conforming to a social norm is more draining and detrimental than beneficial. Here, a reality check is in order. Remember, you just have one life. It's up to you to make the most of it.

Chapter 6

A Killer Diet

"Our food should be our medicine and our medicine should be our food."

\- Hippocrates

Social norms influence our behavior. They can alter how we observe and assimilate beliefs and actions, including how beneficial we deem them. Human motives can be guided by a perceived group norm, even when people have little or no motivation to please others.

This set of accepted rules affects the choices we make on a daily basis. From how we dress to the kind of car we drive, how we behave to how we think, from where we live to, yes, what we choose to eat.

How do Social Norms Influence Food Choices?

Our food choice simply refers to the foods we prefer and choose to buy and consume. There are a complex set of factors that influence our decisions, such as culture, heritage, upbringing, religious adherence, financial standing, price, food allergies, or intolerances.

Personal preferences can be seen in the growing popularity of brands that focus on sustainability, fair trade, organic, or health-related items. Habits, taste, mood, stress, appetite, and cravings play a role. As, of course, do social norms. Social influences can be direct or indirect, conscious or subconscious.

So, how do social norms influence your food choices?

Encourage One to Eat Better

Social norms can have positive outcomes. If you are surrounded by people who encourage healthy eating, you are more likely to follow this path. For example, you might focus on seasonally available foods. Or protein and dairy from animals that are grass-fed or wild-caught. Abundant fresh fruits and vegetables might become your style.

You may decide to eat well to raise your chance of experiencing a longer, happier, disease-free life. On the flip side, you might receive and believe messages that discredit healthy eating.

Peer Pressure

Many adolescents succumb to peer pressure when it comes to food choices. In most teenage groups, the social norm for attractiveness states that females should be skinny and males ought to be muscular. Due to the pressure to fit societal beauty standards and the need for validation, many opt for foods that are low in calories, fat or carbs. As a result, dieting to achieve desired results becomes common.

For instance, the keto diet, the paleo diet, body cleanses with detoxifying tea, the grapefruit diet, binge eating, intermittent fasting. Some youths even completely stop eating. In fact, eating disorders and body dysmorphia are more prevalent in teens and young adults. Clearly, this is not healthy!

There is also a nefarious side to healthy eating: orthorexia. In this condition, one becomes obsessed with only eating healthy foods. The sight, smell, and proximity to perceived unhealthy foods cause distress. Warning signs include:

- Compulsive checking of ingredient lists and nutritional labels

- Increased concern about the health of ingredients

- Cutting out an increasing number of food groups (for example, all sugar, all carbs, all dairy, all meat, all animal products)

- An inability to eat from outside a narrow group of foods that are deemed healthy or pure

- Unusual interest in what others choose to eat

- Spending hours thinking about what food might be served at an upcoming event

- Showing a high level of distress when 'safe' or healthy foods aren't available

- Obsessively following healthy food and lifestyle blogs and social media accounts, like those on Twitter and Instagram

- Body image concerns may or may not be present[4]

Monkey See, Monkey Do

We, humans, are deeply social creatures. When we see someone we admire or whose approval we seek to eat a certain way, it's not uncommon to mimic this behavior. This extends to eating together. For example, if someone orders a particular item, the other is more likely to copy. This can be seen as an evolutionary survival tactic.

In the old days, knowledge of what was and wasn't edible was learned by following local traditions, parents, and community. The lack of laboratory and processing facilities meant the only way to know what could be eaten was by consuming it. Others then ate foods that were found to be safe to eat.

While we no longer consciously subscribe to such thinking, it is still apparent in how we react to the food choices of high-profile celebrities and loved ones. They play a significant role in influencing the foods you desire and the

---

[4] https://www.nationaleatingdisorders.org/learn/by-eating-disor-der/other/orthorexia

quantities you ingest.

Less Time

Lastly is the social norm that connects busyness with success, time paucity with normality. This leads to busy schedules that limit the preference for home-cooked meals. The consequence is choosing unhealthy, processed foods. While the reality might be partially true, it's the mindset which I believe is more harmful.

Processed foods tend to contain higher levels of harmful fats and unhealthy ingredients. These can contribute to higher blood pressure and cholesterol, diabetes and heart disease, increased inflammation and pain, and other health issues.

Unfortunately, it's easy to succumb to these social norms. In doing so, we can make problematic food choices borne on how we see food, the way we perceive time, and the priorities and people in our lives.

Why Do Most People Consume Unhealthy Foods?

As schoolchildren, most of us received a baseline education in nutrition. At least, we are made aware of the supposed healthy food pyramid. But, it's still easy to become confused about what is and isn't good for us. Especially when you consider this untold truth: Food corporations harness smart marketing measures and shady claims to increase profits.

Many "healthier" options are filled with processed, artificial, and dangerous ingredients that your body cannot recognize or digest properly. Yet, as they target convenience and personal ambition, they are often accepted without question.

We, Americans, can be far too polite. We readily submit to the interests of gigantic companies that are invested in the money-making narrative, not your wellbeing. We have also been persuaded — brainwashed — to yearn for quantity over quality.

On the flip side, being aware that one is consuming harmful foods is not always enough to alter behavior. So why don't we stop? The answer to this question is both simple and complex.

In part, we crave unhealthy foods because many contain ample sugar combined with artificial additives designed to taste delicious. This triggers the release of pleasure-inducing neurotransmitters. These foods are crafted in a laboratory to alter your brain to crave and consume more of their products. By using research conducted by food scientists, they are engineered to be irresistible. Blending the perfect proportions of fat, sugar, salt, and flavorings ensures that once you "pop," you literally "can't stop."

However, when someone we know gains weight as a result of the irresistible temptation. What do we say? Something like, *"Boy, did they let themselves go!"*

Processed foods are designed for overconsumption. Then we, ourselves, are programmed to judge. The result is a harsh and vicious cycle.

Instead, we need to meet each other with empathy and understanding. To realize there is more to play than gluttony or a lack of self-discipline. Rather, consumption of modified foods [5]— those that have been shown to create dependence — has increased steadily. If you've wondered why you can't stop at one Lay's or catch yourself licking Dorito dust from your fingers, this is it: They're addictive.

It seems paradoxical that we know certain foods do us, at best, no good, *and* we still struggle to stop eating them. So let's take a closer look at why?

Flavorful Taste

To most taste buds, junk food tastes great. For example, deep-fried foods are more flavorful than bland, steamed, or poached choices. Foods with added sugar, ample calories, and copious amounts of saturated and trans fats, and research-backed flavorings form a delicious temptation.

But it's not just that in-the-moment experience. As we grow up, we become hooked on hyper-palatable products. Sugar-laden, fatty products trigger the brain to release

---

[5]   https://www.ncbi.nlm.nih.gov/pmc/articles/PMC2235907/

neurotransmitters called dopamine and oxytocin. These chemicals induce feelings of relaxation, pleasure, and enjoyment. That's why goods like burgers, bread, cakes, cookies, desserts, donuts, pastries, and pizzas are called '*comfort foods.*' They comfort the emotions... at least temporarily until the next hit.

Visually Appealing

Junk foods are created with aesthetics in mind. Manufacturers use color additives to produce vibrant products that captivate consumers, especially children, and young teens. In addition, we tend to associate color with health. Since ancient times, bright-colored foods have been associated with ripe, ready-to-eat goodness. It's, therefore, in evolutionary terms, sensible to opt for pretty food.

Think about it: Why does a bright red apple appeal more than its pale yellow cousin? That's why foods such as burgers, candies, donuts, ice-creams, pasta, and pizza are all prepared with eye-catching hues.

Perfect for Stress Eating

Our mood affects our choice of food. Psychological stress heightens the lust for junk food. The higher the level of stress, the more likely you are to crave sugary, fatty foods. If chronic, the more likely you are to develop a fast food habit. You may have noticed this yourself.

But why does this happen?

When we are stressed or anxious, we produce a hormone called cortisol. Cortisol increases the amount of sugar in the blood. This is so it can fuel the body's cells; to act as immediate energy to aid metabolism. Cortisol also increases hunger. Ravenously at times!

That's why when we're stressed, we involuntarily opt for foods that are high in fats, sugar, and carbohydrates. This subconscious drive is a hangover from an evolutionary process to aid survival by providing the energy needed to fight or flee. It is not a weakness meant to harm. So the next time you consume foods that are no longer serving you- meet yourself with compassion.

We might also associate unhealthy food with comfort foods. They can induce pleasurable feelings and relax moods. Unfortunately, the search for bliss through food can become habitual, morphing into unhealthy practice.

Easy to Prepare

Junk food can, at first glance, appear to be more convenient. Fast food products are ordinarily easy to grab and consume. This ease can be a major attraction, especially if you work long hours or need to snack on the run.

Like with French fries, their rapid production and the easy storage of packaged products, including soda, are enticing. The combination of availability and convenience, means that junk food consumption and acceptance have become all but ubiquitous.

Affordable

The affordability of junk food has a direct link to its consumption. Cost is an undeniable draw to junk food. It tends to be awfully cheap. In fact, it costs three times as much to follow a healthy diet as it does to eat junk and fast food products.[6]

When junk food is so accessible, convenient, and affordable, it becomes easy to forgo nutritious food. To top it

---

[6] https://journals.plos.org/plosone/article?id=10.1371/journal.pone.0109343

off, it's designed to be scrumptious and addictive. The high sodium sugar, altered fats, and artificial additives might harm your health, but they also powerfully tantalize the taste buds.

Too Busy to Cook

Lastly, many struggle to find time to prepare a home-cooked meal every day. There are many healthful, fast options and ways to lower the time spent in the kitchen. However, you must step off life's rollercoaster for a moment and decide to eat differently before you discover options. Fresh fruit, for example, comes ready packed. Batch cooking can mean a week's worth of meals is created in one day.

Misleading Claims

Food marketing and packaging make eating healthy more difficult. I always become irritated when I see a bag of potato chips that claims, "Cholesterol-free!" Of course, it is! Cholesterol is made in the liver, and since potatoes don't have livers, there will be no cholesterol in that food. Companies smack a large label on the pack, "Cholesterol free!" The aim? To entice people who are either watching their cholesterol or trying to make healthier choices. If it's true that potato chips don't contain cholesterol, why does this superficial claim matter?

The inflammation from the salt, sugar, and fat in the potato chips fuels the inflammatory process. Inflammation in the lumen of blood vessels, which triggers cholesterol to block inflamed regions, enhances coronary artery disease. Potato chips are not heart-healthy!

Clever marketing, with its smoke and mirrors and desire solely for profits, is dangerous. This rampant misleading behavior ought to be criminal!

High Consumption of Junk Food & the Role Sugar Plays in Addiction to Junk Food

Junk food is, in essence, any food that is highly processed, high in calories, added sugars, salt, saturated or trans fats, and very low in nutrients. Junk food is oft referred to as being as addictive as drugs and alcohol.

It is human nature to think about benefits and risks over the short term rather than considering the long-term impact of our choices. This may be partly why millions of people consume junk food. The taste, convenience, and transportable nature are at the forefront. The vast drawbacks of consumption are shunned to the back of the mind. Here, balance is needed. If you wish, enjoy junk food every once in a while. But remember to consider the health impacts.

Look at your overall eating habits and ask:

How often do I consume junk food?

Should I make a change?

Do I consume a balanced, healthy diet?

Am I eating plenty of nutritious foods such as vegetables, fruit, legumes, fish, nuts and seeds, and unprocessed grains?

When it comes to your health, it may seem like you can *"get away with"* occasional junk food when you follow a healthy lifestyle most of the time.

Proceeding further, what role does sugar play in our addiction to junk food?

Sugar is one compound that creates food addiction. It is considered by many to be the biggest enemy to human health as it turns the entire human body and its systems upside down. However, even knowing this, it's difficult to abandon this sweet, irresistible temptation. Sugar is described as a *'bliss point.'*

When we consume sugar, our brain secretes dopamine. Dopamine is a hormone that mediates pleasure. Several studies prove that morphine, heroin, and sugar each trigger the same receptors in the human brain. Thus, we wish to consume more sugar as it provides pleasure and relaxation. However, the level of sugar that makes you, as a consumer happy, is quite high. This encourages food-seeking thoughts and behavior.

It should be noted that the biggest harm caused by sugar consumption is not weight gain or obesity. It's the fact that sugar increases inflammation. Chronic inflammation increases the risk of heart disease, kidney failure, and even cancer.

Let me give you an example of an adored junk food that almost everyone enjoys, regardless of age: Potato chips. This fattening junk food contains salt, sugar, and fat in sufficient measure to trigger addiction. As soon as you eat chips, simple carbohydrates in the potato turn into sugar and provide the hit of pleasure mentioned earlier. After the sugar reaches the blood, the blood sugar level rapidly increases.

Ask yourself, *Is this food taking me closer to my goals or further away?* Most of us want to live a long, well life to maintain a healthy weight and admire the reflection we each see in the mirror. However, I know those who wish to eat junk food, smoke, drink, and use recreational drugs. They understand that these habits will shear years from their lives, and they're fine with that. There is no judgment here. As long you are clear and understand that what you do consistently will either take you closer to or further away from your goals.

If you choose healthily, practice mediation, journaling, prioritize sufficient sleep and love yourself and others, you will create a worthy life and be an inspiration to those you meet. On the other hand, if you choose to eat unhealthily, drink, smoke, party, gamble, and live a selfish life, you may (or may not) be fun to hang out with, but the chances of reaching a happy, fulfilled older age are limited if you make it there. But, back to food...

Unfortunately, we have been conditioned to believe that eating healthy food is time-consuming, expensive, and lacks taste. In reality, this need not be the case.

We live in a world where the right marketing can sell almost anything. This allows companies to achieve unimaginable profits. In the name of cash, adverts are devised to pull the wool over our eyes, so to speak. The result is the massive consumption of harmful foods by our loved ones and us.

However, healthy food does not need to be bland or unappetizing. Nor does it need to be time-consuming. It all depends on the meals you select, how you prepare the food, and the ingredients you choose. For instance, if you're cooking a chicken breast, you can prep the meat by adding flavorful anti-inflammatory spices or herbs, then top it off with vibrant, nicely cut vegetables. Sometimes, garnishing your average foods and experimenting with spices can make all the difference!

If you wish to alter your food habits, foster easy steps that encourage change.

How to Avoid Falling into the Trap of an Unhealthy Diet?

With the very best of intentions and willpower, many fail on the path to an improved diet. This may happen due to easy access to temptation; stores are stocked with seduction. Attending a party, an outing, or a family gathering provides ways to slip up. But, it is our response to the slip that determines how we continue.

Are you generous to yourself, saying: It's okay, I will get back on track?

Or do you keep yourself off track, potentially spiraling into a binge-fest?

Remember, it is what you choose to do consistently that will determine your level of success. As human beings, many of our behaviors and choices are programmed by societal norms. We've allowed junk and fast food companies to invade our lives at every turn. They are almost impossible to avoid. We need to foster change on an individual level. With this in mind, there are ways to avoid getting sucked into the trap of an unhealthy diet. Let's take a look.

Avoid Free Food

As old as the saying goes, *"Nothing in life is free."* That includes the bread basket at restaurants. It might not be added to your bill, but the calories are definitely added to your waistline. The same thing applies to the soda served on airplanes or any unhealthy foods that are given away. So don't confuse free for your wallet with free for your waistline and health.

Stop Getting Value Meals

Have you ever pulled into the drive-thru lane to order a grilled chicken burger, only to pull out with an additional 600 calories added to your order?

Choosing the combo meal may seem like smart financial sense, but is it?

Consuming the extra calories from the medium French fry and soft drink are calories you didn't need. They add a cost that wasn't warranted. In health terms, the cost is high. The next time you eat out, order only what you need to quell your hunger. Start to see the value of saving money along with calories.

Do Not Opt for Food Experiences

From popcorn at the movie theater to hot dogs at a baseball game to drinks at a nightclub, we have been programmed to believe that certain foods enhance the experience. The truth is you, along with others, are conditioned to think that the consumption of certain food or drink is required to enjoy an experience fully.

Refrain from purchasing unhealthy foods, avoid eating mindless calories, and reassure yourself that you can enjoy the movies, sporting events, and parties with or without junk food.

Don't Let Others Influence You

Individual food choices differ depending on the people you are with during a meal. For example, when eating out with friends who order chicken wings, pizzas, and burgers, you might second-guess ordering from the salad menu. This theory is popularly known as the *"I'll have what she's having"* effect.

Being around those who eat unhealthy foods can lower the guilt associated with poor choices and increases the justification for similar behaviors. In addition, it can serve as a form of peer pressure. One simple tip that can help is this: When you are with your friends who eat less healthy, be sure to order first.

On the flip side, being around positive social influences encourages health and weight loss. It's important to surround yourself with individuals who inspire you to eat well and engage in physical activity. With like-minded people who care about their health, it can be just as fun to stay in and cook together as it is to go out.

Don't Be Influenced by Food Advertisements

Regardless of your age, food advertising establishes social norms. So get in the habit of walking away from the television during commercials or pre-record shows so you can fast-forward through the mouthwatering ads.

Remember, when it comes to food, there is always a choice. It's entirely up to you to actively make the right one.

The goal is to base your eating habits on what fuels your health and wellbeing instead of allowing external factors to influence your decisions.

Body Mass Index (BMI) and the Domination of the Industry by Food Corporations

There are ten major companies in charge of the food industry:

- Nestle
- Coca Cola
- PepsiCo
- General Mills
- Kellogg's
- Unilever
- Dannon
- Mars
- Associated British Foods
- Mondelez International

Tobacco companies entered the food industry in the 1980s. The aim? To make their food products as addictive as their cigarettes.

As a result, our foods have been enhanced with addictive substances. The push is to blame you: to promote the false notion that you just lack self-control. In reality, products have been engineered so that when you start eating, you cannot stop. Using salt, sugar, and fats in scientifically determined amounts, they can encourage addiction to their products. This is wonderful for their bottom line, but not yours.

The Body Mass Index (BMI) was invented in the 1830s by Lambert Adolphe Jacques Quetelet, a Belgian mathematician, astronomer, statistician, and sociologist. He was a scientist who applied calculus to human physical characteristics, but it should be noted that he was not a doctor nor studied the physiology of a human under the microscope.

Quetelet was adamant about discovering what an 'average man' would be like. Quetelet is quoted in his book, 'A Treatise on Man and the Development of His Faculties' as, "If the average man were completely determined, we might consider him as the type of perfection. And everything differing from his proportion or condition would constitute deformity or disease ... or monstrosity."

His idea was problematic from the start as it hinted that anyone who was below average to *his scale* was automatically inferior to others. Furthermore, for his study, he used data that was primarily collected from white European men.[7] Thus, this index is steeped in racism and sexism and was used as a scientific justification for eugenics.

In essence, it shows what an ideal *white* man should be like. This may be a surprise to most since it was used so widely. It makes no allowances for people of different races, genders, or physiques. Insurance companies now use BMI to promote fatphobia and charge premiums for individuals with a comparative higher BMI.

The BMI was also used to determine if someone is fat or not supposedly. However, the index is not without other flaws. It does not account for muscle mass. Currently, the BMI shows a range of 18.5 – 24.9 for a *"normal"* person. Anyone below this range is *"underweight,"* while the ones that are above it are considered either *"overweight"* or *"obese."* Almost all professional bodybuilders will be deemed obese according to the BMI chart. Of course, these professionals do not look obese.

If you want a more reliable way to calculate your

---

[7] https://www.goodhousekeeping.com/health/diet-nutri-tion/a35047103/bmi-racist-history/

BMI and determine your propensity for experiencing a cardiac event, opt for the Waist to Hip Ratio (WHR) method.

To do this, you need a tape measure to check your waist circumference and hip circumference. The difference will be assessed and determine if you have a higher likelihood of experiencing an unhealthy cardiac event.

Ways to Calculate Your Waist-to-Hip Ratio

Measuring your waist to hip ratio is simple. Follow these simple steps to calculate it on your own. All you need is a tailor's tape measure and a calculator.

- Stand up straight and breathe out. Next, use a tape measure to check the distance around the smallest part of your waist, just above your belly button. This is your waist circumference. (If unsure exactly where to measure, use the level of the crook of your elbow as a guide.)

- Then measure the distance around the largest part of your hips; the widest part of your buttocks. This is your hip circumference.

- Calculate your WHR by dividing your waist circumference by your hip circumference.

Once you have the result, assess against the chart below to learn what your number means.

Female	Male	Health Risk
0.80 or lower	0.95 or lower	Low health risk
0.81 to 0.84	0.96 to 1.0	Moderate risk
0.85 or higher	1.0 or higher	High risk

Women with a ratio of 0.8 or below and men at 0.95 or below are usually pear-shaped. People with pear-shaped bodies are in the lower risk category for health problems such as heart disease, type 2 diabetes, and some forms of cancer.

Women with a ratio of 0.85 or above and men with a ratio of 1.0 or above are considered to have an apple shape. This is because their fat gathers around the middle. Apple-shaped bodies face a high risk of type 2 diabetes, heart disease, and some types of cancer.

I feel that the hip to waist ratio is far more reliable in helping people understand their bodies in terms of risk. In addition, this measure can help us discover how nutrition can affect long-term health goals without the negative connotations and misinformation associated with BMI.

Use of Additives in Food and Its Effect on Our Diet

Food in America is profoundly processed. Huge corporations that produce foodstuffs prioritize profits over health for their consumers to eagerly incorporate the cheapest ingredients.

When you compare our foods with other countries, you will see the difference. Not only in taste but in nutritional value too.

Countries in Europe use real food ingredients. Freeze-dried strawberries in instant oatmeal instead of flavorings. Beet juice to color red MnMs instead of artificial flavors, like red dye 40, is used in America. This matters for a variety of reasons.

Consumption of synthetic food colors is thought to

cause behavioral symptoms in children.[8] This may be due to chemical changes in the brain, inflammation from an allergic response, and the depletion of minerals, such as zinc, involved in growth and development.

There is a long list of food additives banned in the European Union but have not been removed from the US food production chain.[9]

Food companies also play the system. Rather than remove a harmful compound that has gained widespread awareness, they simply change the name. This makes it harder to recognize the ingredient. For example, red dye 40 is also called:

- Red 40

- Red 40 Lake

- FD&C Red No. 40

- FD&C Red No. 40 Aluminum Lake

_____

[8] https://www.healthline.com/nutrition/red-dye-40#behaviors-in-children
[9] https://www.advisory.com/daily-briefing/2019/01/03/banned-foods#:~:text=Potassium%20bromate%20and%20azodicarbona-mide%20(ADA,goods%20in%20the%20United%20States.

- Allura Red AC

- CI Food Red 17

- INS No. 129

- E129

Until and unless a person knows and remembers all of its names, it is possible to miss the presence of red dye 40.

The role that sugar, omega 6 fatty acids, and grains play in inflammation is also well known. Yet, it is rarely discussed in mainstream media. Clinical nutrition tells us that it starts the arachidonic acid cascade when you ingest one of these pro-inflammatory foods. This will finish by producing pro-inflammatory particles, which induce puffiness, tenderness, and pain.[10]

Sixty percent of calories in the current modern diet come from refined omega-6 oils, sugar, and flour, all of which feed cancerous processes in our cells. While not conscious, the effect is that the average American is pursuing cancer as a dietary goal. In a more positive light, it can also

---

[10] https://www.ncbi.nlm.nih.gov/pmc/articles/PMC6052660/

be said that cancer is vastly more preventable than previously thought. We need to stop feeding cancer and other chronic diseases to live a pain-free and enjoyable life.[11]

Anti-Inflammatory Foods to Add to Your Diet

An anti-inflammatory diet should include these foods:

- Tomatoes

- Olive oil

- Green leafy vegetables such as spinach, kale, and collards

- Nuts like almonds and walnuts (not peanuts)

- Fatty fish like salmon, mackerel, tuna, and sardines

- Fruits such as strawberries, blueberries, cherries, and oranges[12]

---

[11]https://www.dynamicchiropractic.com/mpacms/dc/article.php?id=56065

[12] https://www.health.harvard.edu/staying-healthy/foods-that-fight-inflammation

Be Mindful of Microplastics

It is important to understand the role that microplastics play in our food chain. Bottled water causes the ingestion of microplastics. There are 22 times more microplastics in bottled compared to tap water.

If our water is toxic, how are we ever going to develop robust health?

I prefer to use alkaline water to help with digestive disorders and help keep the body in a state of homeostasis; healthy balance. I personally use Kangan water. Using a water filtration system is better for your long-term health. The impact of water begs the question: How many research projects are currently ascertaining how microplastics affect our health? The answer is zero. This is another example of why you must do your own research and focus on your health. No one will do it for you. If you perform a quick internet search, the results will suggest the jury is still out that science hasn't separated the health benefits of tap water versus alkaline water. However, I encourage you to visit EWG's Tapwater Database and insert your zip code. For my zip code, arsenic is a staggering 558 times the normal amount.

Chapter 7

Your Desires

*"The entire universe is conspiring to give you everything
that you want."*

– Abraham Hicks

So many people lead a life that discourages them
from acting on their desires and passions. But, they're also
actively discouraged from doing so. It's quite sad if you
think about it.

Many of us have allowed ourselves to be controlled
by what society dictates and what families and other people
say. In doing so, personal desires and passions falter. Passions and dreams wither and die.

When you ask people why they're not heartily chasing their dreams and living the life they want, the answer
regularly boils down to fear. But, when we dig deeper, this

fear is most often attributed to judgment by others.

What will they think?

How will I be perceived?

The fear of what others might think or say has suppressed the desires of far too many people for far too long. As a result, the inner question arises: *Has my life had any meaning to it?* It is your desires and passions that sustain, elevate your spirits, and provide a reason to live.

What's key to note is that our desires don't just manifest in our career goals; they apply to our relationships, emotions, mental capacity, and general path in life. To understand how social norms and expectations can make a huge difference here, let's look at the following aspects.

How Social Norms Hinder a Woman's Career Growth

We're often pushed to follow a career that we are not passionate about or even interested in. This is particularly so for women. Following a career in this manner is normal but less than ideal. To state the obvious, the reasons for making such career choices include money and expectations from family and social norms.

Due to these social norms, many find themselves trapped. Specific gender and social norms often significantly hinder a woman's career growth.

How?

Let's take a closer look at how social norms impede a woman's career growth.

No Appreciation for Difference

Firstly, differences between men and women are usually ignored. At times, because we live in a patriarchal society, they are often little understood. Yet, it is in these variations that incredible advantages and findings can be discovered. Therefore, these differences should be valued instead of ridiculed, dismissed, or overlooked.

The differences in the female approach, style, decision-making processes, communication, leadership values, energy, and focus are rarely acknowledged or appreciated. Many mainstream organizations still believe that female work styles clash with their dominant, male-oriented work culture. Social norms fraudulently emphasize that women's leadership style is less effective than their male counterparts when the opposite is true13. This limits growth opportunities in the corporate world, making it infinitely more difficult to climb the corporate ladder.

Pressure to Maintain Perfect Work-life Balance

Secondly, family, life, and work priorities can clash fiercely, not just for women but for men too. However, working women bear the judgmental brunt. Women who work are often assumed to be incompetent at home or unprofessional at work. Criticism is regularly aimed at women around finding the right balance between domestic household chores and work.

No matter what the actual situation is, the fault-finding posse will raise its voice. However, men are not deemed bad husbands or fathers for shirking home duties in order to work late. This biased belief system holds women back from being hired for key positions, suppressing their potential and immense value.

---

13 https://hbr.org/2019/06/research-women-score-higher-than-men-in-most-leadership-skills#:~:text=Gender-,Re-search%3A%20Women%20Score%20Higher%20Than%20Men%20in%20Most%20Leadership%20Skills,analysis%20of%20360%2Dde-gree%20reviews.

Even today, many people still frustratingly adhere to the antiquated norm that states women are better off staying at home rather than working outside.

Limited Career Opportunities

Thirdly, career opportunities for women are also limited. There are more acceptable career options for men than there are for women. Because of this, women who desire a career in a male-dominated industry such as engineering have to settle for the scraps or face indignation and ridicule.

This is often considered "the cost of ambition" for a woman with professional aspirations. This is one reason why there are fewer women leaders and why women are suppressed and cajoled into achieving less in the corporate world. Women are still being sidelined and discriminated against.

For example, here in the States, the importance of time off after having a child is met with scant concern. Requests often fall on deaf ears.

Women are not given sufficient time to rest or look after their children or are told to resign if they "can't manage" work and family life.

The Difference in Pay Scale

Lastly, another social norm that affects career growth for women is in regard to their pay. Some organizations, even today, are underpaying their female employees. Again the false and antiquated belief — the social norm — states that men should always get paid more as they are naturally more hardworking, competent, and driven.

The fact that gender is a factor that affects salaries can drive women from the workforce. This, coupled with limited opportunities, assumptions about their roles, and more, show how social norms negatively impact women's careers and growth.

How and Why Men are Instructed to Hide their Emotions?

It's not just women who face issues. We need to consider what eats away at men's desires to live authentically and why society indoctrinates males to hide their emotions. This starts from the tender age of childhood. For a long time, showing emotions, being loving, kind, and caring have been looked upon as feminine qualities. God forbid a boy is seen as soft!

Because of the way boys are socialized, their ability to competently manage their emotions is systematically undermined. The result is not a macho man; it's an emotionally stunted male who lashes out at others because he cannot properly process and deal with his emotions.

From an early age, men are taught not to cry, not to be *"weak,"* and not to find words to express themselves. Social norms and stereotypes instruct the hiding of emotions. This is, in a word, dangerous. It is imperative that young boys (and girls) are taught emotional intelligence to identify and express how they feel without fear of judgment.

How and why are males pushed to subdue and hide their feelings?

Primary Socialization

Parenting and primary socialization are the first ways males are taught to undermine their emotions. What might this look like? Being brought up in an atmosphere where masculinity is linked to power, and power is seen as men who project a strong exterior.

A strong personality is considered essential for most males from when they were born until they die. Having a strong personality means never appearing to be vulnerable, shedding a tear, or showing signs of perceived weakness in times of adversity. Unfortunately, parents often reinforce the importance of being strong and tell their boys to be rough and tough from an early age.

Secondary Socialization

Secondary socialization plays a part too. The group of male peers further solidifies the message: Hiding emotions to appear superior and manly is what's expected. Those who are honest and open with their emotions are ridiculed and looked down upon.

This further perpetuates the chokehold of toxic masculinity where, in an effort to be male, poisonous habits are developed and sustained. Physical, mental, emotional, and spiritual well-being suffers as a result.

The Idea of the Perfect Man

Thirdly, stereotypes instruct that sentiments ought to be hidden, especially ones regarding sensitivity. For example, the stereotypical man is believed to be lacking sensitivity. In fact, this beautiful trait can be deemed intolerable.

Such stereotypes suppress the ability of a man to express his emotions. So he hides them in the hopes of fitting in. The fear of not being considered sufficiently manly lingers like a dark, grey stormy cloud over most men.

Media Depictions

Moreover, TV shows, movies, and advertisements tend to demonstrate and instruct men to hide their emotions. The usually promoted ideal portrays the singular way a man is supposed to be, what he is allowed to feel, and what he isn't. This is achieved by the roles men play in movies and adverts.

Common examples of these can be seen in James Bond 007, the Marlboro Man who is a gun-toting, cigarette smoking macho man, and basically, any character played by actors like Clint Eastwood, Arnold Schwarzenegger, and Sylvester Stallone.

These numerous influences reinforce primary and secondary socialization in instructing men to hide their emotions.

However, more people are becoming aware of the negative effects of placing such expectations on men. Being able to cry, laugh, show kindness, and express any emotion ought to be allowed, regardless of gender.

Luckily, the idea of what a man *"should"* be is changing. There is growing acceptance for men who are comfortable expressing themselves, those who aren't afraid to show they care.

How Social Norms Affect Dating Life and Relationships

Everything down to our lives' paths has an expected outcome. You are supposed to leave home, go to college, get a decent job, start a family, and so on. When you interact with others, there are a set of expectations too.

- Is it a birthday party? You had better bring a gift.

- A family member's in the hospital? You should visit.

- Rounding the corner at a certain age? Then marriage should be on the horizon.

There are plenty of unhealthy social norms that influence how we interact with each other and, therefore, how we develop relationships. Yes, including how we date.

Expectations for Physical Affection

Now don't get alarmed; I'm not suggesting that you should stop physical affection in a relationship. The problem is in the *expectation* of physical affection. This can be detrimental to your relationship without your realizing it. It's imperative that you discuss this with your partner. Determine the amount of physical contact you both enjoy and then deliver. Otherwise, one person might feel unwanted or rejected, and the other may feel uncomfortable due to excess physical contact.

Why? Because it's a norm to expect that once you're dating someone, you must get physical. In fact, for many, this can be a programmed and subconscious response. In some cases, a person might feel entitled to a physical relationship, whether their partner is ready or not. If you find yourself feeling disappointed or frustrated that, even after considerable time, your partner is not reciprocating in the way you want, it may be because of this social norm.

If you remain unaware, your relationship could start to fester. Don't let the expectation or experience of physical affection become unhealthy because of an entrenched social norm. Take your partner's consent and preferences into consideration and remember, it is always okay to establish and assert your boundaries!

If your partner is less affectionate than you, they're probably showing their affections in other ways. Look for these instead of feeling upset. If you don't know your own or your partner's love language, read the book, *The Five Love Languages: How to Express Heartfelt Commitment to Your Mate* by *Gary Chapman.*

Stifling Gender Norms

Gender norms are always problematic, mainly because they tend to be archaic. Thus, it can be difficult to break free from them. Similarly, it's customary in relationships to fall into traditional gender norms. As a matter of fact, this holds true even in same-sex relationships. One person is supposed to be the breadwinner while the other is expected to look after the house.

It's also a given that the woman will complete the domestic work. This can create unfair pressure for either party in the relationship to behave in a certain way. As a result, one person often becomes weighed down.

Today, couples are beginning to break free from this stifling mold. Stay-at-home dads with breadwinning wives and households where both people share responsibilities are becoming normalized. In a healthy relationship, it's not about the person's gender but invested time, effort, and equality.

Doing Things for Show

There's ample pressure to put on a good face. And it's not just you that has to look good anymore; your relationship does too. While this has been endemic for an eon, it has gained traction since the introduction of social media influencers who show off their happy, picture-perfect families in million-dollar mansions with thousand-dollar smiles.

This might be why you feel the need to say that everything is fine, even when it isn't. What makes this an unhealthy social norm is the way it ignores real issues. These internet celebrities reveal only snapshots in a highlights reel. It encourages people to only focus on what's outside and not intrinsic to the relationship. If this is your focus, you will find yourself with a hollow, shallow, unfulfilling love life.

This outward-facing relationship makes it difficult to be open with your partner about your feelings. It leads to disconnection as they will never know what you need. Remember, mind reading isn't possible. You must stop expecting it! Building a connection that's pretty on the surface is not life-affirming or embedded with longevity. If you want something to last, work on it in private. As an unimportant consequence, it'll look so good that others will notice. No Instagram posts will be necessary.

Masking Emotions

The social norm for men to repress and not express emotions will likely affect their dating life in miserable ways. We discussed this in detail, but it is worth mentioning again. Consider it a gentle reminder that men are allowed to feel and share too. For men, it can be harder to talk because of their conditioning against it.

What took years to learn takes time to unlearn. Be patient with your male partner. Provide space and encouragement to open up. Look to yourself and ensure your communication is solid and fluent. Together, work on improvement in this field and on understanding each other.

Additionally, remember that you can always say no. Your relationship should be secure enough for you and your partner to effectively express not just love and happiness but anger, sorrow, and melancholy emotions without fear.

Unrealistic Depictions of Love

Lastly, the norm states that love is all you need. This idea has made many relationships collapse. In an ideal world, love alone could solve all things, but not in this one. The average household has to pay bills, feed mouths, and clothe bodies. One needs a solid career path, goals for the future, financial stability, and emotional maturity to take relationships to the next level.

Media depictions often create unrealistic expectations. Think about the storyline where the girl drops everything for the guy or vice versa. They fight against the world and their families to be together. Examples are littered widely in media. In F.R.I.E.N.D.S, Rachel left her promising new career to stay with Ross. In Titanic, Rose was convinced she could be with Jack simply because they were in love.

Romeo and Juliet; we know how that ended.

Besides the clear flaws to this premise, it's a toxic social norm because a person needs more than love to exist. Food, shelter, clothing, and money are required along with understanding, mutual respect, a foundation of trust, honesty, transparency, sacrifice, and compromise.

Challenging Social Norms about Mental Illness

It seems every time someone behaves unusually, the term mental illness is raised. The actions of an unreliable politician, a parent who flees with their child, a mass murderer, or a socially awkward person, or those who don't easily fit in with regular society (and so, societal norms) are often falsely attributed to mental illness. Conclusions such as these do nothing for people who experience real mental illness.

Those with mental illnesses face great stigma. A diagnosis doesn't mean destructive behaviors. Nor the engagement in an endless pattern of treacherous, unpredictable, or irrational behavior. *"Normal"* people exhibit such behavior at times, too. This is human nature. Instead, the misconceptions show that most people have a limited understanding of what mental illness really is.

Unlike physical diseases, mental illnesses are invisible ailments; they do not have outward signs on the body. This can create a lack of awareness because it's harder for people to empathize with and acknowledge its existence when a condition can't be seen. Bias develops that can worsen the affliction. In addition, mental illness can be overwhelming. It takes considerable energy to simply keep a job, maintain personal care, attend therapy sessions, and take medications on time. This does not leave much room for more.

Challenging social norms on mental illness is necessary. The way we see and perceive each other must change. We are all connected, and you are part of the solution. The next time you assume another has a mental illness because they behave in a way that is not consistent with predominant social norms, stop. Rethink your analysis and understand this is not what constitutes a disorder.

Throwing around uneducated opinions makes it difficult for people who live with these conditions to function in society. The vast majority of mental illness diagnoses are not accompanied by dangerous behavior. Similarly, the vast majority of people without mental illness aren't inherently menacing. Everyone suffers at some point or another. It is our collective responsibility to meet each other with compassion and love.

In conclusion, people need to be given the freedom to live the way they desire. It's high time that each one of us starts to live a more fulfilling life. That we engage in activities that we are passionate about. Be it selecting a career, choosing not to enter into a relationship, or behaving in a way that does not conform to social norms.

You get one life. You don't need anyone's approval for what you do with your life. We need to stop caring about other people's opinions and instead focus on what makes us happy and content. It is our job to raise the collective energy. To live every day with authenticity in a manner that honors you. Instead of waiting for the perfect life, create it. Enjoy the things you desire. Those that make your heart sing. Break free; challenge social norms. Especially those that offer you little benefit!

Chapter 8

The Soulful Cleanse

*"Edit your life frequently and ruthlessly. It is your master-
piece after all."*

- Unknown

What does spirituality mean?

The definition is quite broad and open to interpreta-
tion based on a person's beliefs. However, to define it
simply, spirituality relates to the innate connection one has
to one's soul or the spirit. The relationship to our essential
being rather than the ones we develop with material, physical
items. It includes a sense of or belief that we are part of
something bigger than ourselves. It ties in with the search for
meaning and purpose. To some level, it's a universal human
experience that touches us all.

Being spiritual provides immeasurable advantages.

For example, taking back control of your life may seem daunting, especially if you've been walking the path of others' expectations. Yet, spirituality provides a way to gradually and gently wrest back control. In fact, being spiritual can clear your head, help you re-evaluate where you are in life, and begin the task of walking to the beat of your own drum.

So now, the question here is, how does being spiritual help you do just that? Spirituality helps you cleanse your mind and soul to raise awareness and clarity. To provide different lenses so you can see your truth. It profoundly alters how you perceive and experience life.

The accompanying insights show you how to regain control rather than continue to relinquish your power. In reference to this, I would like to introduce the term *spiritual cleansing.*

What is Spiritual Cleansing?

It's a type of energetic healing that aims to identify and cure the spiritual cause for any problem that has manifested in your life. For example, suppose you struggle to clear your head and take charge of your life. Traditional approaches will often fail to instigate change because they rarely tackle the root problem. Here you can turn to spiritual cleansing to identity the cause and solve it from deep within.

Spirituality will allow you to restore a lost sense of purpose and find meaning in life again. When you take this route, you will begin to realize and reflect on many things: The kind of thoughts and emotions you entertain, the quality of your life, how negativity hinders positivity, how worldly desires and problems interfere with your happiness, and how you show up in your life. It's often difficult to think straight when negative thoughts and feelings run rampant in your mind or when you are unsure of your purpose in this world.

One of the biggest blessings I see in my life and those of my spiritually engaged patients are in terms of clarity. You will realize how to be positive instead of negative. This alone can transform your life!

Have you ever stopped for a moment to look at the circumstances and people around you? If negative people and experiences surround you, your physical and emotional energy will likely be drained. Therefore, stepping back from negativity is not just empowering for your soul; it speaks volumes about the life changes you wish to make because you must free yourself from defeatism to achieve.

As your problems disappear, there will be more time to pursue what you want in your life. You will make room for positive people and experiences to come to you.

You can only achieve clarity when you pay close attention to what is and what deserves to be on your mind. To truly know what benefits you. Spirituality helps you do this. It nourishes and recharges your thought processes and actions. When you focus on a state of calmness and regularly practice positivity, your life will change. As your mind becomes clear, you will mentally relax and experience serenity. This is absolutely empowering! Who doesn't want to be empowered?

It's possible to no longer feel snowed under by life, find areas that would benefit from a change, and learn how to take charge. As you become empowered, your desires and dreams will be more likely to manifest. You will notice the real root of your concerns. Together, this will allow even greater clarity. You'll notice a shift in perspective; instead of only focusing on the what-ifs and unmet desires, you will see the bigger picture.

This ensures you are not causing a life of confusion

or overthinking in certain areas. As we discussed at the beginning of the book, we need to name our goals to work toward them. Clarity is essential for this process. You can then
do two things: break concerns down into manageable,
achievable tasks and bring the bigger picture back into focus.

Being spiritual will also enhance your self-awareness. This will help you to recognize areas where you are
subconsciously giving away your power. Becoming self-
aware isn't as hard as it sounds. By simply making an effort
to observe your feelings and thoughts, you will learn whether
you lean toward life's positive aspects or whether you get
weighed down by negative thought patterns.

Autonomic negative thoughts (ANTs) are sadly quite
common. You have most likely encountered ANTs in your
daily life. For example, someone doesn't text back and
leaves you on read. You assume they are mad, think we are
losers, or they are just plain over you. In actuality, they are
consumed with their life and harbor no ill toward you.

Observe your thoughts without judgment. Your job
is not to stop thinking about the ANTs but to recognize them,
and if the thought is no longer serving you, let the ANTs drift

off like clouds in the sky and make room for positive thinking and healing.

You cannot expect a future free from negative experiences, especially if you continue to give control to others. But, through the practice of identifying and relinquishing negativity, you can change the narrative. It's time to take back control, including your thoughts, and begin to create the future of your dreams.

Self-awareness is part of this process. It allows you to view negative aspects that affect your mojo and figure out effective measures to combat them. You can recycle negativity into positivity by using positive affirmations and spirituality. Positive affirmations will help lift your spiritual energy to a higher level and allow you to manifest a life you love.

Sometimes using affirmations can feel disingenuous, depending on where you are during your spiritual journey. This is when '*iffirmations*' come into play. *Iffirmations* are different from affirmations by using the *IF* question.

I can highlight this better by showing you an example of an affirmation and *iffirmation,* which can give you a better idea. An affirmation would be:

I focus my attention on the things I can control and release the rest.

In contrast, an *Iffiramtion* would be:

What If I focus my attention on the things I can control and release the rest?

You can use both tools to help guide you in life. As stated above, spirituality can transform your life. Once you begin a regular spiritual practice, watch how it enhances your life. From small, daily activities to the wonder of an expansive life, get ready for a massive shift.

How Mindfulness Yoga & Detachment Helps You Achieve Inner Peace

Mindfulness has always been an essential aspect of the practice of yoga. The difference between mindfulness yoga and other yoga practices is that this variant is mainly focused on enhancing mind-body awareness instead of the alignment and improvement of one's posture. The focus is on the cultivation of present moment awareness to observe rather than react through watching both mind and emotions while in a yoga pose, without judgment and to practice patience and discourage reactivity. In return, one becomes less responsive to negative stimuli off the mat.

Raises Deeper Sense of Awareness

Mindfulness provides one with a deeper sense of awareness. The practice expands your perspective, awareness, and understanding of who you are—training your awareness aids a shift away from negative characteristics that hold back your growth. Those characteristics like making you play the victim, blaming others or resisting the ebb and flow that is always happening around you.

You'll be amazed at how such a simple practice helps you face everyday challenges with ease! This will be noticed in all areas of your life: your relationships, work, social life, and leisure activities. Through the practice of mindfulness yoga, you can learn to let go and accept situations for what they are.

Unlocks Acceptance

Acceptance is known to ease depression. For instance, when you begin to accept your depression, you start to remove its power. Soon you will realize that it is simply a thought and a feeling; it is not you.

Practicing acceptance on the mat prepares you for real life. You truly do not get to choose what's going to happen next seamlessly. Life chops and changes. So, acceptance teaches you to roll with the punches that life throws your way.

Heightens Sense of Compassion and Non-Judgement of Others

Mindfulness heightens your sense of compassion and non-judgment of others. Increased kindness, empathy, and understanding can be taken from the mat and carried into your everyday existence.

Yoga and mindfulness work together to help you achieve a higher level of awareness, peace, and connection between your mind, body, spirit, and others.

Gives More Control Over Your Thoughts

Mindfulness yoga is a great way to attain inner peace. Practicing stillness has been proven to work for many individuals. While practicing stillness, aim to meditate, be calm, and focus on the thoughts you have running through your mind. You can then observe your thoughts and filter them out as you please.

For example, let the unhappy, negative, and stressful ones flee far away and gently encourage happy thoughts to take their place instead. Observing your thoughts in this manner is necessary because only then can you identify and understand what lifts you and what weighs you down.

Taking a Closer Look at Detachment

When it comes to detachment, most people usually focus only on the dictionary meaning. Unfortunately, its negative connotations can make people apprehensive about this wonderful practice. In order to use this tool to benefit your mental and emotional health, a correct understanding is important. With this in mind, what exactly is detachment?

In essence, detachment is a form of non-attachment that allows a person to overcome their material desires, worldly concepts, or lust for others to attain a higher perspective. It's a beautiful, healthy way to take a step back from a scenario and check in with yourself to ensure you are healthy, happy, and sure about the current situation.

Detachment is especially necessary in today's busy world, where we each face excessive stimuli. Furthermore,

the single-minded drive to do and achieve more can be kept
in check with some healthy detachment. But, like all good
things, moderation is key.

One walks a fine line with detachment because, in
excess, it can lead to the development of an avoidant attach-
ment style. However, if you are aware of how you incorporate detachment and couple it with mindfulness yoga, you
can truly reap incredible benefits.

Using Spirituality to Embrace Your Feel-ings and Desires

Daily spiritual life can be complicated, to say the
least. Each day we face encounters that challenge our feelings, desires, hopes, plans, and motivations. Spirituality can
be used to embrace your desires; those longings that lay deep
within the human heart. For example, the desire to live a
happy life, be at peace, be surrounded by family and friends,
and closeness to the Lord (Source, Universe, Gaia, Mother
Nature).

We all want to be loved, be accepted for who we are,
and live a life of freedom, peace, and joy. All desires are

founded in hope. Aspiration is the first signal that God is close at hand. By taking note of our daily desires and sharing them with God, we complete the first step in our daily spiritual journey. As you invite spirituality in, you can embrace your desires with open arms and visualize, then manifest their reality.

On the other hand, emotions can, at times, be terrifying and overwhelming. You may experience guilt or shame for choosing yourself over others because you have always prioritized everyone else's needs first. Once you focus on self-love, self-compassion, and prioritizing pleasure for yourself, you can give to others from your full cup. Your anxious thoughts will diminish, and you will feel fulfilled. If you get trapped between hopeful desires and the fear of challenges, complex emotions can derail you.

Remember, *"they"* govern us with division, polarity, hate, and fear. The answer is love- love for yourself and others. Honor your natural emotions that arise within. The feelings that linger from yesterday might inform your desires for tomorrow. Remember, also, that a feeling is fleeting. Feel the emotion in that moment, but don't burden yourself with carrying a negative thought for the rest of your day or your life, for that matter. Don't let an emotion define who you are.

By harnessing your spirituality, you can become in tune with your desires and feelings and, thus, you can embrace them.

It's vital to let go of negative feelings to make ample room for positive ones. When you cling to pessimism, it clutters your mind, clouding your thoughts, actions, and experiences. It pulls you out of the bliss of mindful being. Instead, act optimistically. Positivity is both a requirement for and a result of spiritual life. If you carry the burden of despair, this can greatly hinder your ability to connect with and live through spirit.

The Universal Force of Love: Albert Einstein's Letter to His Daughter

Love is one of the most beautiful, fulfilling, and powerful emotions in this world. Love is the emotion with the absolute power to move mountains and make the impossible possible. I adore the famous letter that theoretical physicist, Albert Einstein, wrote to his daughter about the universal force of love…

When I proposed the theory of relativity, very few understood me, and what I will reveal now to transmit to mankind will also collide with the misunderstanding and prejudice in the world. I ask you to guard the letters as long as necessary, years, decades until society is advanced enough to accept what I will explain below. There is an extremely powerful force that, so far, science has not found a formal explanation to. It is a force that includes and governs all others and is even behind any phenomenon operating in the universe and has not yet been identified by us. This universal force is LOVE.

When scientists looked for a unified theory of the universe, they forgot the most powerful unseen force. Love is Light that enlightens those who give and receive it. Love is gravity because it makes some people feel attracted to others. Love is power, because it multiplies the best we have, and allows humanity not to be extinguished in their blind selfishness. Love unfolds and reveals. For love, we live and die. Love is God, and God is Love. This force explains everything and gives meaning to life.

This is the variable that we have ignored for too long, maybe because we are afraid of love because it is the only *energy in the universe that man has not learned to drive at will. To give visibility to love, I made a simple substitution in my most famous equation. If, instead of $E = mc^2$, we accept that the energy to heal the world can be obtained through love multiplied by the speed of light squared, we arrive at the conclusion that love is the most powerful force there is, because it has no limits.*

After the failure of humanity in the use and control of the other forces of the universe that have turned against us, it is urgent that we nourish ourselves with another kind of energy...

If we want our species to survive, if we are to find meaning in life, if we want to save the world and every sentient being that inhabits it, love is the one and only answer. Perhaps we are not yet ready to make a bomb of love, a device powerful enough to entirely destroy the hate, selfishness, and greed that devastate the planet.

However, each individual carries within them a small but powerful generator of love whose energy is waiting to be released. When we learn to give and receive this universal energy, dear Lieserl, we will have affirmed that love conquers all, is able to transcend everything and anything, because love is the quintessence of life.

I deeply regret not having been able to express what is in my heart, which has quietly beaten for you all my life. Maybe it's too late to apologize, but as time is relative, I need to tell you that I love you, and thanks to you, I have reached the ultimate answer!

Your father,
Albert Einstein

Now, it should be noted that there is some ambiguity regarding the authenticity of this letter. Many historians claim that Einstein did not write it. However, the letter's existence first became known when his step-daughter, Margot Einstein, donated some family letters to the Hebrew University.

It's clear to see that Love is a universal force. Even though invisible, its presence is always felt in some form or the other. Albert Einstein's letter on the universal force of love might make you look upon love in a new light. Regardless of whether the letter is authentic or not, it holds a beautiful message. The premise of love conquers all is an inspiring and uplifting one.

Inner Peace is the New Epitome of Success, and Kindness is the New Definer of Beauty

Inner peace refers to a state of being mentally and spiritually at ease with having enough; enough knowledge and understanding to keep oneself strong in the face of any discord. It means:

- Not overthinking

- Not over analyzing

- Not scurrying from thought to thought

- Not constantly dwelling on hurts, real or perceived

- No longer spending precious energy and time on unimportant or meaningless ideas

The values of our lives today are different from those of yesterday. Today everyone is busy chasing monetary success. It's sad what most people believe to be the epitome of having *made it*. The pursuit of luxurious cars, a handsome wage, branded outfits, and premium lifestyles had led to robotic, hectic, and stressful lives, devoid of true fulfillment. In lusting after monetary success, inner peace has crumbled.

Yet, along our errant path, some people have started to notice and question this reality. I believe times are changing; definitions too. Inner peace is becoming the new definition of success.

Why is Inner Peace the New Epitome of Success?

Inner peace is, or ought to be, the new definition for success for the following reasons...

Inner peace is a state of mind. It reveals your personality by how you react to positive and negative energies. It alters how you see and relate to the outer world around you. It radiates mental health and assists you in achieving harmony within your mind, body, and spirit. When you are truly at peace, you are able to:

- Make better decisions

- Harness optimism

- Be more creative

- Remain focused

- Increase your productivity, and

- Experience a happier, healthier life

Inner peace builds your self-confidence, stabilizes your mind, and purifies your character. The fact is that no matter how much money you have, if you lack inner peace, your wealth will remain a superficial blessing. Inner peace can't be bought; that's what makes it so precious. Those who have inner peace have achieved true success. They truly have it ALL.

Reasons Why Kindness is the New Definer of Beauty

To me, the concept that kindness is the new beautiful is irrefutable. Kindness makes you beautiful, no matter your external appearance. Kindness is often called *the small coin of love*. This word is normally designated to little deeds of thoughtfulness and gentleness. Kindness is one of the most worthwhile ideals to practice, indulge in, and spread.

Loving tenderness is not present in everyone. At times it can feel rare. The world needs kindness in handfuls as it leaves a great impact, like the lingering presence of gentle Gaia. It's the little gestures like holding a door open, saying thank you, or smiling at a stranger that count. The inherent goodwill piles up positivity in your life in small assured amounts. In the end, your material wealth will not be remembered. What will matter, and what people will recall is how kind or unkind you choose to be.

Kindness is absolutely the new beautiful. If you wish to leave a long-lasting, loving impact on people once you've passed and if you wish to be remembered well, practice kindness in every moment.

Forgiveness – A Form of Self-Love

Did you know love can be felt on a micro level, starting from yourself? I want to share a key aspect of love: forgiveness (or, in this case, moving forward and forgiving yourself). It's essential that you excuse your human failings. Forgiveness is an enriching action in our lives. One that's hard to make real progress without. If you continue holding on to past misdeeds, you will break your self-esteem and silence the opportunity to find out who you truly are and who you can be.

Holding a grudge or remaining upset and attached to something that happened ten years ago is not healthy. It stunts your emotional health, locks you into that scenario, and makes it impossible to learn from your mistakes.

As you surrender the past and embrace freedom, you will find peace of mind. Remember that forgiveness is a sign of strength. The practice of relinquishing guilt emanates from spirituality and gifts you control of your life.

Furthermore, forgiveness shows responsibility. It allows you to decide what will happen next and to step into the light of your God-given existence.

To truly forgive yourself, you must become aware of your limitations and understand who you are. Remember, with kindness, to err is human. No one is perfect, even if they appear to be at first blush. Viewing yourself as an imperfect being who intermittently makes mistakes will allow you to embrace the art of self-forgiveness. This will light the path for a beautiful tomorrow.

Benefits of Spirituality on Your Mental, Emotional, and Physical Health

Spirituality creates a deeper bond with yourself and offers various mental, emotional, and physical benefits. By incorporating spirituality into your life, you will naturally reap the benefits.

Curious?

Here are some of the major advantages.

Helps Reduce Stress

Firstly, it helps to calm stress. Emotional tension has many triggers, including the negative stimuli around us and circumstances outside our control. Practicing spirituality is a productive way to focus your energy on positive and find respite, particularly during stress. It also aids mental clarity, which can help you to uncover a feasible solution to the problem.

Lowers Depression

Secondly, it reduces depression. Depression can be treated with medication and talk therapy. Remember: Spirituality is never a substitute for professional therapy or medication prescribed by your therapist. However, certain spiritual practices, such as mindfulness meditation, yoga, and prayer, can work synergistically with your therapy to alleviate the effects of depression. For example, yoga, which combines movement and breathing exercises that promote calmness and flexibility, has been scientifically shown to alleviate the symptoms of depression[14].

Decreases Your Blood Pressure

Spiritual people tend to have lower blood pressure[15] than those vested solely in the material world. Reducing stress levels through spiritual practice lowers one's blood pressure. Again, this is not a substitute for professional medical advice. Yet, it offers hope and options for those seeking a natural approach.

Improves Life Expectancy

There is a greater life expectancy[16] rate for spiritual

---

[14] https://www.ncbi.nlm.nih.gov/pmc/articles/PMC5871291/
[15] https://www.medicalnewstoday.com/articles/260699
[16] https://parallelyoga.ca/3-scientifically-proven-ways-that-yoga-helps-us-live-longer/

beings. Thus, the benefits of being spiritually healthy are profound, with the potential to enhance every aspect of your life.

So, seek others with a positive vibe. This will ease your ability to remain positive, too. As this practice becomes a habit, it will permeate your body. You will soon begin to think, feel, react, and behave positively. You will elevate yourself and your chance of living a longer, happier, and healthier life.

Every single person has a story. You can make yours great by beginning today, starting with your soul. Remembering that a calm mind, a fit body, and a house full of love can not be bought- they must be developed over time. Now that you've learned this information, ask yourself, *do you have any reason to wait?*

Chapter 9

Giving Back

"For it is in giving that we receive."

- St. Francis of Assi

What's the first thing you want to do when you receive amazing news? You reach out to someone important to you and share it with them. Now, what if something horrible happens? Again, you reach out for support. We each rely on the people we love for emotional and mental support during both the good and bad times.

The need for connection is ingrained in all of us. It is what defines man as a social animal. No one can flourish or attain true happiness in isolation. This instills in us the desire to give back; to be there for others through life's ups and downs, just as they are for us. As people living in a community, we have an innate need to contribute to the betterment of those around us. It can be expressed in the form of a small act, like being there for a friend in need, or a massive undertaking, like contributing your time and finances to a worthwhile cause. Through the act of giving, you realize how much difference you can make to another human life.

The Importance of Giving Back

Have you ever wondered why it is so important to give back to the community? Spending time enriching society broadens your perceptions of the world. By surrounding and immersing yourself with people who are whole-heartedly dedicated to bettering the world, you can learn so much. In addition, you start to gain a distinct sense of purpose by serving those around you, which often manifests in other areas of your life.

Unquestionably, it's also essential for your community. Without volunteers, many of the events and services you enjoy would not be so readily available in your communities. For example, spending time helping out at local shelters or food banks and giving to charity provides a vital service to the less fortunate in your community.

The secret to living well is in giving. If you think about it, what is life all about? It's about creating meaning.

How do you create meaning in your life? It's not just about what you do for yourself, but for others. Yes, you should prioritize self-care, but giving doesn't require a focus on one person alone.

Once your basic needs are met, such as a roof over your head and healthy food in your belly, it is rewarding to give back to people within your community. Remember, others lack access to the advantages and resources you take for granted. If you wish to make a difference in people's lives elsewhere in the world, this is possible and rewarding too. Either way, you can start at any level where you feel comfortable.

Giving back helps to unite communities and bridge economic, social, and political gaps.

Unfortunately, some social norms might prevent you from living your life to the fullest. For instance, let's suppose you have ample wealth and wish to help the poor by providing financial assistance. Social conditioning may stop you in your tracks. Why? Our individualist societal values might encourage you to focus on a decrease in your wealth or trigger thoughts that you are not responsible for others. In this way, the rich keep getting richer, and the poor keep becoming poorer.

However, if you open your eyes and reflect on giving back, you will see the truth. You can prevent social norms from negatively influencing your life and the lives of those you have the capacity to help.

Easy Ways to Give Back to Your Community

Some ways and steps you can take to start giving back include the following.

Find Your Purpose

First and foremost, find your purpose. Ask yourself questions like:

What really motivates or drives me?

Am I encouraged by a hefty salary in my job?

Why do I enjoy making money?

Is it because it enables you to provide for yourself and your family and to feel secure?

Do I enjoy being recognized for my accomplishments?

Maybe you relish recognition because you feel like you're making the most of your time and expertise or because you enjoy giving back to your industry in some way.

There's always a greater purpose that drives your actions. Therefore, you must find and evaluate that purpose.

Finding the answer to the questions above forms the backbone to the question: *How can I give back to society in a meaningful way?*

When you contribute to your community in this manner, you will experience a greater sense of fulfillment. You will feel like you're making a significant difference for a good cause. Ultimately, this will also bring you closer to achieving your personal goals.

Start Now

The second tip is to start now. Even a small step forward matters. If you're not currently giving back, it isn't necessarily because you don't have sufficient money or time. A lack of resources is not the reason; instead, a lack of *resourcefulness*. Many people wait to give back, but the truth is, no matter what resources you have, you can start today.

The contribution you make enables you to devote at least a small part of your life to helping others. And it has little to do with how much you have. So whether you earn $20,000 a year and donate your time to volunteering at a local community center, or you take home $1 million annually and donate a portion to a cause close to your heart, there are ways you can start helping others now.

Rely on the Ripple Effect

The third point is to create a ripple effect. Think about the people that you admire. What do these people regularly do? They work diligently to spread their message and create value in the lives of others. They prioritize giving back to society. Now, think about the positive impact these people have (or have had) on the globe. You may not have the same means to give back, but that doesn't mean your contribution is small or insignificant.

As you start giving back to the community, you will see how your positive actions encourage others around you to get involved, too. Giving back allows you to create a ripple effect of positive impact, inspiring others to do the same.

Finding What Fits

Giving back is about finding a fit between your passions and how they can meet a certain need. There are multiple ways to contribute, so take the time to find out what works best for you.

Look for an area of philanthropy that speaks to your heart and soul.

- If you love children, seek ways to give back to your community's schools

- If you love gardening and planting, assist in beautifying local parks and waterways

- If you're on a limited budget, consider donating your time or making use of your network to facilitate others' contributions

- Acts of kindness such as recycling or visiting an elderly neighbor go a long way toward giving back to the community

When you find opportunities that fit your ideals and your lifestyle, you will discover a way to contribute without stretching yourself too thin.

Unlock Your True Potential

Embrace your life as a resource. If giving back sounds like a feat reserved for heroes, that's misconception speaking. The reality is that everyone's life experience is unique, and yours uniquely equips you with skills and a perspective that no one else has. Remember, you do not have to be "perfect" to give back.

Learn self-acceptance, and embrace all that you have to offer. Know that it is enough. The significance of giving back shouldn't be ignored or overlooked just because you don't feel ready. Not only will your helpful actions benefit those on the receiving end, but you will also discover a personal sense of joy and fulfillment through your contributions. This, in turn, will allow you to unlock your true potential.

Learn to Give Back Regularly

Once you cultivate the habit of giving back regularly, even if your contribution is small, it will begin to feel natural and simple. So start contributing to the world around you today, and get ready to reap the benefits of giving back tomorrow.

Remember: Even if you don't feel like you have a lot to offer, try to give back as often as you can. Even contributing your time on a quarterly basis to a cause close to your heart matters. You will lift both yourself and others up as you do so.

Know Yourself

As instructed at the ancient Temple of Apollo at Delphi, *"Know thyself"* is an essential quest in the journey of a well-lived life. Getting to know yourself is also fundamental when it comes to giving back. When you understand the driving force of your inspiration, you identify how to give in a meaningful and sustainable way.

When you look at your community, it can feel like too much requires your attention. However, when you know yourself, you can narrow your focus to where you are best able to contribute.

Instead of becoming overwhelmed by the multitude of needs, find what truly speaks to you. Your actions, then, will be performed by inspired love and be genuine in nature. This will raise your impact and make meaning in your life.

Corporations: Their Influence on Social Norms

Large companies are uniquely positioned to drive change around social norms by using their brand, credibility, access to key influencers, marketing expertise, reach, and financial power. As a result, these corporations can create significant, lasting social change but, instead, often distill harm.

How does this happen?

Let's say you see two laundry detergent ads on TV. What makes them different? One ad may provide factual and functional information about its product. The other taps into the accepted norm that women, specifically mothers, are responsible for the laundry. They reiterate archaic stereotypes in order to promote sales and, in doing so, perpetuate harmful gender norms. Even though laundry might seem like a small issue, these types of ads contribute to a raft of ever-present expectations and depictions that build on one another. In this example, they give breath to the misguided concept that a woman's place is in the home.

Let's consider another example. Certain corporations feature dark-skinned women to advertise beauty creams that lighten the skin. In doing so, they reinforce the problematic social norm that fairer, lighter skin is akin to beauty.

Not only does the promotion of these stereotypes undermine confidence, but it can also alter people's beliefs about what matters. Beauty has nothing to do with the color of a person's complexion.

Everyone is beautiful in their unique way. We, as individuals and a society, need to break away from these undue influences. When a corporation promotes these social norms, do not buy in. Raise your voice. Write and speak out. If it's in your heart, support charities and causes that fight this behavior. And, simply, vote with your wallet by choosing ethical companies instead.

Why Is Giving Back the Greatest Gift?

Give back to the community, those you love and care for, and your family and friends. Community outreach can be your legacy if you invest in giving back regularly and passionately. Remember your purpose and remain on your path. You were brought into this world to live a good, meaningful life, to help others, to spread kindness, to learn and grow as a human being, and to make the most of your time on Earth.

However, most people forget this: In the end, you won't be remembered by how much wealth you had, what clothes you wore, or how big your house was. Instead, you will be remembered for who you were as a person, the noble acts you performed for others, for your compassion, giving heart, and for the quality of your character.

Stop for a moment and ask yourself these questions:

Do you wish to be remembered as someone who accomplished great things?

Do you want to fade into history, unremembered?

Giving back will be remembered. Others will speak highly of your generous, loving heart and soul even long after you pass from this world to the next.

By giving back to the community, you accomplish masses. You lift a burden from someone's back. Spread joy. Ease pain or difficulty. Show that you care and value those around you without the need for personal accolades. Your actions can create a great legacy. Start today. Make your mark in wonderful and positive ways. Surely, others will follow your inspired lead.

Chapter 10

Do You Know Your Core?

"You are only as young as your spine is flexible."

- Joseph Pilates

Do you ever wonder what your "core" actually means? Or, more specifically, what the difference between your physical core and core desired feeling is? Strengthening your physical core while living in accordance with your own specific core desired feelings will allow inner peace and contentedness to permeate your soul.

Your physical core is also called the powerhouse. The midsection of your body incorporates central muscles on the front, back, and sides. This group of muscles stabilizes the spine and pelvis for dynamic activity; it supports you as you move by stabilizing the entire body. The muscles include the transversus abdominis, rectus abdominis, internal and external obliques, lumbar multifidus, erector spinae, diaphragm, and pelvic floor.

Importance of Core Exercises in Strengthening Your Physical Core

Why should you spend your precious time adding these exercises to your lifestyle? Firstly, core exercises improve balance and stability and strengthen your frame. They train the muscles in your hips, lower back, pelvis, and abdomen to work in harmony. The result is better balance and strength, whether on the playing field or in daily activities.

Secondly, they don't require specialized equipment or a gym membership. You can hone your physical core at home. Any exercise that uses your abdominal and back muscles in a coordinated fashion acts to build your core.

Examples of core exercises include bridging, planks, sit-ups, and stability ball exercises. Suppose you choose to incorporate free-weight exercises while maintaining a stable trunk. In that case, you can multi-task and train multiple muscles, including those of your core as well and upper and lower extremities. When you have strong core muscles, physical activities become easier. Everything functions better, from your golf swing to reaching for a glass from the top shelf or bending down to tie your shoes.

Weak core muscles leave you vulnerable to poor posture, lower back pain, and muscle damage. In contrast, a strong core results in less fatigue, greater endurance, and fewer injuries. As a nice aside, they'll help you reach your fitness goals and stay in shape.

Your Emotional Core (Core Values)

We live in a fast-paced and constantly changing world. Its constant evolution while we try to make sense of life can feel overwhelming. However, most people maintain their core values. So, what are core values?

In simple terms, core values are beliefs or principles that are held most dear. They are of central importance to how we navigate life. They act as a guiding light. Your emotional core embodies all facets of emotional management. It's the primary driving emotion behind a person's thoughts and behavior.

This includes identifying and responding to your feelings, the process of emotional fluidity, and keeping in touch with how you connect to and experience life. A healthy emotional core is central to psychological wellbeing.

Ideal core values are highly significant because they act as a compass in the journey to an amazing life. They will improve your decision-making ability, productivity, lead to greater achievements, and perhaps, most importantly, enhance your ability to love and be loved. Your core values, in essence, define the person you are.

You might find yourself sharing similar core values with your parents, or they may be different. Your core values should be named and written down in your journal so you can change, update, and respond to how these make you feel. Remember, self-care is the new health care. You need to define what is important for you and name what feeling you are working toward.

This is immensely helpful when deciding how to make your next move. Just ask yourself...

Is this in accordance with my core values?

Will this decision bring me further away or closer to my goal?

This habit makes indecision a thing of the past. When you are prioritizing your own happiness and inner peace, you will always be making the correct choice. Here is a brief list of basic core values that you might resonate with.

Discipline. Control over one's self can lead you to the life that you desire. This is a valuable core value. It has been said that discipline equals freedom because if you can apply discipline to the right areas, you will free yourself from pointless pursuits. Discipline in earlier life means more freedom as you age; physically, psychologically, and spiritually. Discipline to save now means more financial freedom in the long term. And it goes on.

Empathy. It allows you to connect on a deeper level to the people you are closest to and those you have not met. Empathy is a grounding force that provides clarity, connection, understanding, and inspiration. Practicing empathy requires awareness that others, like you, have a worldview based on their experiences. These may be different from yours, and that's okay.

Gratitude provides a powerful perspective shift whenever you feel stuck in a rut. By being grateful for the big and small blessings in your life, like having access to food, water, clean air, shelter, a job, and loved ones, you can embrace the bounty you already have as well as attract more.

Humility is the antidote to arrogance and selfishness and is a value that, if adopted, will keep your feet firmly on the ground. Being humble is appealing and keeps your ego in check. Remember not to take life so seriously. We are literally flesh bags with a spiritual center being hurled through deep space on a rock we call Earth. Laugh, dance, and remember we started as stardust, and at our death, we will return to dust.

Peace is a core value that takes years of practice to perfect. However, its rewards are endless. Peace enables clear decision-making, freedom of thought, and action and provides a deep understanding of the extraordinary life that you have been given. When you are at peace, life will proceed more smoothly.

Compassion refers to taking time to understand the suffering of others and acting on it. This one value could alleviate much of the world's struggle and suffering if incorporated en masse.

Moderation is key, as wise people have noted since ancient times. A lack of moderation can deliver damaging consequences, especially for your health. So make life fun and live it the way you wish, but live in moderation to realize the value of items and avoid wastage.

What Is Your Life Philosophy?

The philosophy of life refers to the mental framework for understanding how the world works and how you fit into the world. Your philosophy includes deciding what is good or bad, what success or failure looks like, and your purpose here on Earth. Each person has their own unique outlook on life, which makes the philosophy of life so special. A personal philosophy helps you wander correctly and respond to random stimuli with little impact on your long-term goals.

Robert Byrne once said, *"The purpose of life is a life of purpose."* In order to get somewhere, you need to define and decide on your end goal. The sooner you reach your definition, the clearer everything becomes. A life without a purpose is a life without a destination.

Your purpose is to find and engage in the things that bring you joy, laughter, and a feeling of timelessness. Move into exploration and experimentation and enjoy the journey. You can't force the discovery. It may come tomorrow, next month, or next year. But search, still, for clarity. When you have identified yours, it is infinitely easier to deal with doubts, remain on track, keep your focus, and continue moving forward.

Living with a purpose means living intentionally. If you don't yet have a philosophy of life, sit down, unwind, and reflect. Write down your thoughts. Seek a clear understanding. Once identified, you will know which way to move forward.

Remember, it's your life at the end of the day, and you should navigate the controls. Own who you are, what you stand for, and indulge in what makes you happy and adds meaning to your life. Live fearlessly. Don't let society or social norms dominate and determine your life. Take a strong stand for yourself. Life will be as hard as you let it be. But, in all honesty, the secret to leading a good life is in your hands; it all begins and ends with you.

Pause for a moment and ask yourself,

Would you prefer to let this life go, to waste it feeling sorry and miserable for yourself?

Or would you rather rise above and live life on your own terms?

ENGAGE YOUR CORE & OTHER LESSONS FOR A HEALTHY, HAPPY & WELL-LIVED LIFE

You have the power to live the life you've always dreamt of. All it takes is a leap of faith and courage to push you forward. You must be motivated and inspired, driven, and willing to make this life of yours. If you want to be healthy, eat well, and exercise if you want to choose a different career, jump!

Don't limit yourself to those social norms. If you want to get married at 50, go for it. If you're going to be remembered, do meaningful things. If you want to be happy, surrender unnecessary fears. Change begins and stops with you.

Live your best life, the way you want, and on your own terms. I promise it will be one of the best choices you make for yourself!